Body Piercing

"Does it hurt?"

A complete illustrated guide
to Body Piercing

by Mark Eames

Illustrations by Laura R Eames

NliteN Publications, England
www. nliten.co.uk

This book emphasises the need for safety precautions, the use of an experienced body piercing operative, and the importance of proper equipment and techniques. Even if the cautionary advice is followed, body piercings involve physical risk. The author and the publisher specifically disclaim responsibility for any adverse effects or unforeseen consequences resulting from the use of any information contained herein. The reader is advised to consult his or her regular doctor immediately if any complications arise.

This book is an original NliteN publication.

BODY PIERCING - "Does it hurt?"

First published by NliteN publications in Great Britain in September 2001

Copyright © 2001 Mark Eames

ISBN: 0-9541138-0-2

NliteN Publications
68 High Street
Cosham
England
PO7 6ET

For information:
Telephone: 023 9237 7099
Visit: www.nliten.co.uk
Email: booksales@nliten.co.uk

Printed in England

To:

Michelle for first encouraging me to write this book and the effort she has made in providing me with the time to bring it to fruition.

Laura who set me on the path towards body piercing and whose artistic talent has provided the illustrations to my text.

For the foresight and belief of the directors of Body-shock, as well as their kind support and assistance in bringing this book to the market.

And the thousands of people that I have either pierced, photographed, or talked to, each of you has contributed in making this book possible.

To each and all, I offer you my deepest heartfelt thanks.

Contents

Foreword

In recent years, the practice of body piercing has shown a remarkable increase in popularity in the UK, and probably in most of the Western world. However, as Mark Eames points out in this excellent – and essential – guide, the practice is not only very old but also widespread. Ancient civilisations certainly used it, and I was interested to read, for example, that a mere 2754 years ago, Roman centurions had their nipples pierced when newly promoted. They then apparently hung their military capes from the piercing to show their superior courage. (I only received a paper diploma when I qualified as a doctor!)

I first became interested in skin piercing when, about 20 years ago, I investigated some outbreaks of hepatitis type B (jaundice associated with liver disease, which can be fatal). These outbreaks were caused by various skin-piercing practitioners – not body piercers as it happened, but they did illustrate what could happen with unskilled piercing. I then produced some guidelines for hygienic skin piercing, which at that time covered tattooing, acupuncture, ear-piercing and hair electrolysis. These guidelines were used throughout most of the country, and the rarity of outbreaks after this showed that spreading these serious infections could be avoided. One or two small outbreaks that occurred were caused by not following the guidelines, rather than a problem with the guidelines themselves. In 1990, I produced some guidelines specifically for body piercers.

Body piercing can be done safely – by a good practitioner. Unfortunately, when there is a rapid burgeoning of anything new, some poor practitioners appear with the good ones. This book will help anyone who wants to be pierced to learn about it first, and to know what to ask for and look for in a practitioner. First of all, you want it to be safe. Safety these days is not just about hygiene – it is also about making sure the right jewellery and instruments are used for the piercing; and about making sure the piercer knows his or her trade, in particular about anatomy. Secondly, you want to make sure the piercer will perform to ethical standards.

Hippocrates, the Greek 'Father of Medicine' who lived around 400BC, in his ethical guidance for doctors stated right at the beginning, 'First, do no harm.' This should apply not just to doctors, but to all professionals. The body piercers studio should be bright and spotless. He should be happy to show you that he uses an autoclave or pre-sterilised needles to prevent hepatitis or HIV (the virus causing AIDS). He should give you clear aftercare instructions – how to keep the wound clean and dry, and how to look after it generally. He should be happy to see you if there is a problem, and show necessary care, even if he has to refer you to a doctor. He should use hypo-allergenic materials for his piercings, especially for any jewellery he inserts. Nickel allergy in particular is fairly common and can be avoided for the most part. He should be able to tell you about the type of piercing you want – what are its good and bad points, and whether or not it is suitable for you. He should know what parts of the body not to pierce – for example, the outer quarter of the eyebrow can be pierced safely, but the inner quarter has an important artery and nerve and must be avoided. He should also ask you about what illnesses you may have in case there is any medical reason why you should not be pierced.

The professional ethical body piercer will not pierce those obviously under age, or those under the influence of drink or drugs, or those who are obviously being pressurised into a body piercing they do not want. He will understand Mark's good sensible advice to you – do not rush into a piercing. Although it is not as permanent as a tattoo, it can still leave a scar, and why go through the pain and suffering if you did not really want it in the first place?

But if you do want a body piercing, or are unsure about it, this is the ideal book for you to read. It covers what you need to know, in clear simple language. It even tells you which are the most painful piercings, and which hurt less than you think. You will find the sections on the different types of body piercings particularly useful, I think, and I strongly suggest you do not ask to be pierced in any part of the body not mentioned in this book.

I am delighted to be able to recommend this book to you, and, if you do decide to have one, I wish you a safe and satisfying piercing.

Norman Noah, MB, BS, FRCP, FFPHM
Professor of Epidemiology and Public Health
London School of Hygiene and Tropical Medicine

Consultant Epidemiologist
PHLS Communicable Disease Surveillance Centre, London

September 2001.

How to use this book

This book is set out in such a way that, for you the reader, each chapter becomes a check list of what to expect before, during and after a piercing procedure. It aims to improve your understanding and, in so doing, maybe raise your expectations. With increased knowledge you can do a lot to help maintain high standards in the practice of body piercing. When used correctly, the information inside this book can help you avoid any unnecessary pitfalls, which can occur when choosing a piercing.

Being a current practising body piercer, my inside knowledge can give you invaluable insights into the piercing trade, preparing you for your experience and hopefully starting you off on the inside track towards a successful and enjoyable experience. Choose only piercing operatives that meet these newfound expectations.

When thinking about having a piercing, first look it up in chapter 8, entitled 'Types of piercings'. Then, when you have selected the type of piercing you want to have, you will need to find out how best to look after it in chapter 9, 'How to care for a piercing'. Check for any possible implications and potential complications in chapter 10, entitled 'If things go wrong' and find out how best to avoid these problems by reading, 'Things to consider before having a piercing' in chapter 5.

Having read these chapters you will now have a better feel for the implications of your piercing, but you still need to know what body jewellery to wear in your piercing. You will find this out by reading chapter 4, 'All about body jewellery'. If you are still happy with your choice, you will now need to read 'What happens during a piercing?'. To find out about the legalities of body piercing, then read chapter 3, 'Is Body piercing legal? – The law'.

When you have read 'Why do people do it?' in chapter 1, you will have a wider understanding of the experience that you are about to share, whilst maybe empathising with, millions of others who are doing the same thing. Finally you can explore the origins of your choice in chapter 2, 'A brief history'.

You are now fully briefed and ready to find a piercing operative. You will know how to spot a good one after reading chapter 6, 'How to spot a reputable body piercer'. By brushing up on the 'Commonly used piercing terms' and 'Frequently asked questions' in chapters 13 and 14, you will know exactly what to ask, and be starting to sound like a seasoned body piercer.

If you are an experienced body piercing operative then you will realise that this is not an exhaustive body piercing list. This book is intended as an introduction to body piercing for the beginner. It is not a technical guide to the actual carrying out of body piercing procedures. The practice of body piercing should only be attempted by a person after they have gained substantial knowledge in human anatomy and physiology, hygiene, infection control and piercing techniques. Then it should first be carried out under the supervision of an experienced piercing practitioner.

If, while reading this book, you come across any unfamiliar technical words or phrases, you will find them listed, together with their meaning, in chapter 13, 'Commonly used piercing terms'.

Have a safe and enjoyable piercing!

Introduction

This book is based upon my own experiences of body piercing, both as a concerned parent and later as a practising body piercing operative. My experience began when my then 13-year-old daughter asked to be pierced. Her request was initially met with a horrified – 'No way!' Over the coming weeks her persistence paid dividends, and gradually the 'No' mellowed to 'When you are older', and then a somewhat camouflaged yes with, 'When you are 16 years old'.

I was concerned for her health, I knew there were dangers of disease transmission, but I didn't have the knowledge to identify the necessary procedures, or how to measure standards in hygiene and the difference between good and bad piercing practices. As well as the obvious surface health issues, something else troubled me at a deeper, more emotional level.

Whenever the subject of her navel piercing came up, these deeper concerns surfaced, bringing intense feelings of anger and annoyance. I was surprised at the way I felt about body piercing and began to search within myself for answers. My thoughts lead me back to when I was an architectural student at university and my first encounters with body piercing. Images of campus parties and rock concerts with provocatively dressed followers of Punk Rock came to mind. These people challenged all my childhood values. Their aggressive dance routines usually involved throwing each other from the stage into the audience below. From dark corners emerged the ominous red glow as large safety pins and other sharp objects were heated under the flame of cigarette-lighters, before being plunged into a nose, ear, nipple or goodness knows what else.

These images of over twenty years ago had coloured my view ever since of body piercing, and whenever I met people who dressed or acted in similar ways to these college-day punks, I considered them to be threatening. They belonged to a strange kind of cult or tribe who refused to conform and therefore were a threat to society as I knew it.

Were these people really a threat to me and society? Of course they weren't. I had since met and worked with people who dressed in an outrageous fashion and who had been pierced, and they were normal caring human beings, often more considerate than most. As I began to balance these two diametrically opposed sets of images, the realisation began to dawn that they frightened me. These feelings of anger and annoyance at the very mention or sight of body-pierced people were the result of my own suppressed fears. My biggest fear was that my daughter, by taking up the symbolic tokens of this wayward pierced tribe, was about to discard the values that I had consciously tried to teach her.

Inadvertently, my daughter had started me on a journey that revealed both my own prejudices and those of society. I had rejected piercing out of hand and dismissed it as an adolescent fad. I had also pigeonholed those who were pierced as fringe extremists who ought to be treated with disdain.

Five years on, I have thrown off such petty, limiting views and have developed a deeper understanding of the people who choose to be pierced, as well as the people who pierce them. Indeed, as a practising body piercing operative who has carried out thousands of piercings, I have become one of their number. In working to make the practice safe, it is my wish to bring body piercing firmly back into the central core of mainstream life, by the spread of information about the important issues involved in body piercing.

Exiled to the fringes of society, body piercing has been starved of the support of key mainstream organisations, particularly in the fields of medicine, public health and the media. This environment of ignorance has all too often been the birth place of myths and fallacies.

As a body piercer I am able to give insights into the piercing trade that would not ordinarily be available. In sharing some of my experiences, it is my hope that these myths will be dispelled and information will replace ignorance and suspicion. Knowledge and confidence will enable people to experience body piercing safely and avoid the potential dangers.

Chapter One...
Why do people do it?

IN MANY PARTS of the world, in so-called primitive cultures, body piercing is an integral part of daily life. For instance, when a child of the Brazilian Suya tribe listens to and follows the advice of the village elders, they receive an ear piercing as a symbol of their achievement in learning to listen. These ritualistic piercings are often referred to as rites of passage, and are used to mark significant events and changes in a person's life. The progress of an individual through birth, puberty, marriage and finally into death is often marked by rituals that sometimes include a piercing as part of the ceremony.

In the Western world, the motivations for being pierced are not steeped in any local traditions. Such ceremonies have long since been given up and forgotten. A piercing is often regarded by mainstream society as a statement of individuality, separateness and rebellion. However, the individual often has a piercing as a sign of recognition of a personal achievement as opposed to rebellion.

In the absence of a traditional social framework that charts a person's progress through life, body piercing gives the opportunity to create one's own rites of passage.

The renaissance in the use of body piercings as social statements is practised by all sorts of individuals. Short, tall, slim and fat people get pierced for their own, very different reasons. Body piercing cuts through all social barriers, with school teachers, lawyers, doctors, nurses, bank managers, building labourers, shop workers, mothers, housewives and children all being pierced. Although many men do have piercings, the vast majority are women, Western piercing being very much a female-led phenomenon.

For some, it's the look and the idea of being seen to be at the cutting edge of fashion; others get a buzz from the rush of adrenaline that comes when the needle passes through their flesh. Being pierced helps some to feel that they are making a statement that sets them apart from the rest of society. Whilst often, for teenagers, the motivation is fear, a fear of being different from the main group. Not being pierced sets them apart from the group. Sometimes teenagers have a piercing in order to rebel against their parents' or teachers' conservative values.

The need to rebel, whilst at the same time wishing to belong to a small select group, finds expression in more extreme forms of group piercings. The use of a routine, ritualistic piercing as an initiation rite is popular with the inner city gangs of the USA, and is not yet commonly found in Britain.

Age is very quickly becoming less of a barrier to being pierced. Back in the mid 1990s, piercing was the domain of the teenager. Since then, the number of older people with piercings has been steadily rising. In any piercing waiting room it is common to find men and women of all ages. There is no upper limit, with sixty-, seventy- and even eighty-year-olds enjoying piercing.

Sometimes people choose to have a piercing to mark an event in their life, often symbolising a change in their circumstances. It might be the end of a relationship, through death or separation, or a new beginning – starting a job, entering into a relationship, the birth of a child or the creation of a 'new me'.

For many women the process of re-creation begins with, and is symbolised by, a navel piercing. The female midriff holds a major social and personal significance in Western societies. Many life changes are apparent by alterations in the shape and appearance of the female tummy. The young flaunt it, showing it off between crop top and tight fitting jeans. Motherhood announces its arrival on the stomach in the form of stretch marks. With the passage of time, middle age often announces its arrival by spreading these marks even wider, and the effects of gravity carry the sagging tummy even lower.

Over time, not only does the body change shape, but the person's mind evolves. A need develops to express oneself in a new found role. For the teenager, having a navel piercing is often made as a choice of fashion. By the time a person reaches their late twenties and early thirties their reasons for having a piercing become much more representative of life's changes. At forty, the navel piercing can take on talisman-like qualities; the hope is for time to stand still or even go into reverse. She is making a final gesture of indignation in the face of the inevitability of the passage of time.

Men also use body piercing to alter the way others perceive them. The fashion is most popular amongst young men, but not so popular with older males. A common reason behind being pierced, as well as wishing to be seen to be cool, is the oppor- tunity to reinvent oneself, the motivation being that a piercing can help present you as more exciting and perhaps as more wild and dangerous, usually in the hope of becoming more attractive to the opposite sex.

Sometimes couples go together to have joint piercings as a sign of their commitment to each other. Older couples in more established relationships often take part in joint piercings, where both partners undergo piercings of an intimate nature. Piercings of the penis and the clitoris are proving increasingly popular amongst this age group, often reintroducing spice and a sense of excitement back into what might have become a stale relation- ship. Even engagements and marriages are performed where the conventional ceremonial wedding rings are replaced with skin piercing hoops.

It should now be apparent that body piercing is not just a fad of fashion being practised by a few teenagers, or extremists rebelling against conservative values. Piercing is becoming recog- nised as a personal statement marking an individual's passage through life's experiences, and for many it is a tool through which they find a means of expressing their own inner sense of being.

Chapter Two...

A brief history

When did body piercing begin?

BECAUSE THE RE-BIRTH of body piercing has occurred so rapidly in Western society, very little is written about the history of body piercing. It was only in the last decade of the 20th century, when body piercing thrust itself into the theatre of mainstream life, that the question started to be asked, "When did all this begin?".

The answer is that, ever since people 2.5 million years ago walked out of the jungles of central Africa and began using the natural objects that they found around them as tools, body piercing has never stopped being practised.

Indigenous primitive peoples

It is important to realise today that, in many traditional primitive societies, skin piercing still plays an important role. In these cultures, piercing will often take the form of a ritual that has deep spiritual significance to the individual, and brings recognised status from other members of the social group.

For the Bundi tribe of Papua New Guinea, a piercing of the nose septum symbolises the passage of the boy into manhood. Once this piercing rite as been performed he is then treated differently by the tribe – as a man rather than as a boy. Similar kinds of piercings traditions are practised in all parts of the world including Africa, South and North America, Asia, the Pacific islands, and even in the mountains of Eastern Europe. In some cases, these piercing traditions have been carried down through generations for thousands of years.

The link between past and present piercing traditions and modern 21st century living is encapsulated in two movements that use body piercing as an integral part of their beliefs and life styles.

Neo-tribalists

People who incorporate the traditions of other cultures with futuristic visions of the human race are referred to as neo-tribalists. They look to other cultures from all parts of the world to provide established customs and practices, linking past and present in order to bring meaning into their own lives. Various rituals from these different cultures are adapted, offering individuals a variety of opportunities for personal expression. These often include piercing practices.

Modern primitives

Rather than translating primitive cultural practices into high tech modern life styles, modern primitives seek to preserve this diverse heritage. They found their beginnings in the hippy movement of the 1960s and came to prominence during the late 1980s and early 1990s.

Flower power seeds of the piercing renaissance

Throughout the 20th century, Westerners have been piercing themselves and each other, but the practice didn't galvanise into a cohesive movement until the last quarter of the century. The seeds of the modern renaissance in popular piercing were sown in the 1960s. When the hippy travellers of the 'flower power' era encountered piercing customs in India and the Far East, these practices were brought back and integrated into Western life styles. Piercings, amongst many other practices, became at this time symbols of freedom and rebellion against the dark forces of conservatism. A progressive extension of hippy revolution saw its expression in the Punk Rock movement of the late 1970s, where everyday objects such as safety pins were used as piercing jewellery.

S&M

In the 1970s, whilst most of the fringe members of the hippy movement became integrated within the conservative mainstream of society, a few of the remaining hard core followers began to focus their activities around the city of San Francisco in the United States. This whole region became the focus for all sorts of radical fringe movements, including the 'gay rights' activists. The piercing ring became an intrinsic symbol of membership of these movements.

A social offshoot of the gay rights movement was the exhibitionist pseudo-violent sub-culture, the members of which became known as Sado-Masochists, abbreviated to 'S&M'. During the 1980s the movement became the vehicle for gay expression and extremism. Its appeal then broadened to include hetero-sexuals. Many members of this social sub-culture lived, by day, normal and sometimes high profile mainstream conservative lives. Under cover of darkness, basement clubs and meeting houses provided an outlet for otherwise suppressed, and often extreme, forms of sexual and physical expression. Participants engaged in activities where the fine line between pain and pleasure became blurred. Piercing the flesh and wearing body jewellery was an integral part of the experience. Body piercing and sado-masochism quickly became synonymous.

Sexual pleasure

The use of body piercing as a tool to achieve heightened sexual pleasure is nothing new in the west. Ladies of the court of the

14th century Bavarian Queen Isabella indulged themselves in the erotic fashion of exposing their breasts. For the externally prudish members of Victorian high society, body piercing was an essential prerequisite to an evening of passion and heightened sensual pleasures. Their outward appearance claimed the moral high ground whilst, at the same time, they lived a private life that plumbed the depths of sexual debauchery. Writing at the time, a distinguished Victorian gentleman described the sensation of touching his nipple ring as being electrifying, and referred to it as being a light switch to an erection.

Gang culture

In the last quarter of the 20th century, body piercing and tattooing have become essential symbols of gang membership. Bikers and inner city gang members have used piercing as part of initiation rites for new members.

Specialist publications

Throughout the period of the 1980s and 1990s a variety of specialist magazines contributed to the growth of interest in body piercing. Each issue introduced to the reader new and fascinating insights into piercing types and new jewellery advances, as well as making each and every reader aware that they shared common experiences with other like-minded people. This form of networking helped build and link together vast numbers of otherwise separate isolated individuals.

Supply and demand

During this period people were learning piercing skills from self-piercing experiments and as occasional or part-time body piercers. Jewellery was generally hand made, or adapted to suit the specialist piercing need. With the increase in popularity of piercings, demand was growing for more sophisticated forms of body jewellery. To meet this need, specialist manufacturers began to spring up. When, in the mid 1990s, wearing piercing jewellery became a necessary fashion accessory, the combined forces of supply and demand created the vehicle for the modern piercing renaissance. The systems of manufacture were in place to quickly produce and supply jewellery to the millions of people who wanted it. The number of people wanting piercing initially over-whelmed those able to perform the piercings. In situations where demand outstrips supply, there is always the temptation for the fly-by-night operator to take advantage, which in some cases did happen.

Piercing renaissance

In most primitive cultures, body piercing is carried out as an open integral part of the social fabric. Western piercing, however, has often been maintained in underground movements. Despite count-less acts of persecution it has survived many years, and today it is revived. When super-models Chirsty Turlington and Naomi Campbell appeared on the catwalk at a London fashion show in 1994 wearing navel barbells, body piercing was for the first time thrust under the spotlight of mainstream media. The role of navel barbells as a cool fashion statement was further rein-forced when pop stars like Madonna and Janet Jackson quickly followed suit.

At the beginning of the 21st century, body piercing has captured the imagination of millions of individuals. The practice permeates all strata of mainstream society, yet few seem to notice how far it has spread and still treat those that are pierced as though they are members of extreme groups from the fringes of society. The integration of body piercing as being a part of the social fabric of a modern advanced society has deep-rooted precedents.

Ancient civilisations

In the ancient civilisations of Sameria, Egypt, Greece and Rome, body piercings were commonplace. Navel piercing was revered as sacred in Egypt, where the Pharaohs and the priesthood had their navels pierced to aid the passage from this world into the afterlife.

The Mayan civilisations of central America shared similar spiritual body piercing traditions, and virtually all parts of the body were pierced.

In ancient Rome, Emperors wore gold ear jewellery, and their centurions displayed nipple rings as a sign of their superior courage. Both Greeks and Romans pierced the genitalia of their slaves to encourage chastity and to prevent their reproducing.

In the Middle Ages, people in Europe believed that demons could enter the body through the left ear. Men therefore wore earrings to keep these demons away.

Our piercing heritage

The social history of body piercing is waiting to be written. There is a need for archaeologists to re-evaluate existing finds, asking the question: Is the split ring that they have unearthed an item for fixing or fastening a garment, or could it have had a deeper, more penetrating purpose? No doubt many a historian has uncovered more than one reference to some fascinating skin piercing episode, only to discard it later as irrelevant to their work. All these small finds are important clues and, pieced together, they can help create a wider vision of the so far untold story of our own body piercing heritage.

Chapter Three...

Is body piercing legal?

The law

ALTHOUGH THE ROOTS of body piercing are ancient, dating back thousands if not millions of years, the recent resurgence of interest in piercing has occurred at a phenomenal speed over a very short period of time. The Western body piercing trade is still young, and it will take time for the systems of regulation to take a hold of the issues. In the meantime these are the main issues and current laws.

In Britain, premises where ear piercings are carried out must be registered with a local authority, but there is no national legislation specific to the practice of piercing other parts of the body. Some people, in particular those engaged in public health, are concerned about the massive growth in body piercing. They fear that without legislation the trade will fall below the necessary standards in quality and service.

New body piercing legislation is not a high Government priority, and any future laws are likely only to extend 'The London Local Authorities Act 1991', an existing licensing scheme that currently operates in the capital.

Age of consent

The age at which it is either legal or appropriate for someone to be pierced is a burning issue in any body piercing debate. Unlike tattooing, where legislation imposes a lower age limit of 18 years on persons to be tattooed, body piercing has no such lower age limit. At present, under common law, if the child is capable of understanding the nature and implications of the procedure, they are regarded as being of an age to consent. However, this doesn't apply when piercing male or female genital organs, including female breasts. Such a piercing carried out on a child under the age of 16 years could be regarded as indecent assault. Parents or legal guardians are not permitted to consent to this type of piercing on behalf of a child under the age of 16.

In other parts of the world, including Europe and Australasia, the demand for piercings has been as large as in Britain. Governments in these countries are in a similar position and are in the process of deciding how best to deal with the massive growth of the trade. For instance, in the United States of America, Congress has not set any national law, allowing each state to determine law locally.

In Europe some countries have come close to banning body piercing. The danger in any ban would be to push body piercing back into the fringes of society, thus making it an underground activity where it could continue and thrive uncontrolled.

The consumer has an important role in determining the standards in body piercing by making themselves aware of the current issues, and by asking the right questions. This book is intended to inform the reader of the issues, and provide a guide to enable them to make safer choices.

Chapter Four...

All about body jewellery

THE CONSTRUCTION OF body jewellery is very simple. In principle it is made up of two main types of component: a length of bar, and one or two balls. If the bar is straight and threaded at each end, and balls are attached to the threads, these are called barbells. Where, instead of being straight, the bar is bent to form a curve, this is called a curved barbell and, if the curve forms a ring, it is called a hoop or a BCR (Ball Closure Ring). BCRs have small round balls called beads placed in between the two ends of the hoop to complete and secure the ring.

All kinds of body jewellery are from one of these two families, either barbells or BCRs. For example, a barbell that is curved, with a small threaded ball on one end and a larger crystal-set ball at the other, is called a Jewelled Navel Bar, abbreviated to 'JNB'. As the name suggests, a JNB is worn in the navel.

Types of jewellery

Here are some of the more common members of the jewellery families.

Ball Closure Ring 'BCR'
or Captive Bead Ring 'CBR'

This is what most people refer to as a ring or a hoop. The BCR has a small section of the hoop left out, and is designed for a small bead to be clasped into this section. The bead has two small holes or dents drilled into its surface. These dents enable the hoop to clasp it in place. Opening a BCR can be very tricky, especially when it is inserted into a piercing. Specialist ring opening pliers are used to make this process safe and easy.

Barbells

Straight barbell

A length of bar, usually metal and threaded at both ends, is called a post. Threaded balls are then fitted to both ends of the post to complete the barbell. Threads on balls are generally designed to tighten in a clockwise direction.

Curved barbells

These are barbells that have a curved post running between the two balls. The balls on barbells can be of different sizes and shapes.

Navel barbells

Navel bars are curved barbells that are fitted with two different sized balls. A smaller ball usually fits at the top of the navel piercing and a

second larger ball at the bottom. If the bottom ball is jewelled then this is called a Jewelled Navel Barbell, shortened to 'JNB'.

Labret stud

This is a barbell with a threaded ball at one end of the post and a fixed flat plate at the other. These are used where a normal barbell is likely to be uncomfort-

able to wear. For example, having the ball of a barbell between your lip and teeth could be very uncomfortable and might rub away gums and tooth enamel. The flat plate of the labret stud is less obtrusive and sits more comfortably in the mouth.

Balls and beads

The difference between a ball and a bead is determined by the way they attach to the jewellery. Balls are threaded so that they will screw onto the threaded post of a barbell. Beads are drilled to create small dents or holes at the two opposite sides, and are designed to fit into the missing section of a BCR to complete the circle. As well as metal, beads and balls are made of all sorts of materials, including natural crystal, wood and plastic. Ease of cleaning is important with a fresh piercing, and non-porous materials are less likely to harbour germs. For this reason metal balls and beads are advised to be worn in all initial piercings.

Sizing jewellery

Gauge

This is the measurement that tells you the diameter (thickness) of the bar and applies to both barbells and BCRs. The gauge of the piercing jewellery is very important. If it is too narrow, the chances of the jewellery moving or cutting through the skin are high. Narrow gauge jewellery in the wrong piercing can cut through the skin in much the same way that a metal wire is used to cut through cheese. When this happens in a piercing it is termed the 'cheese wire effect'. Consulting an experienced piercing operative before selecting any new jewellery for a piercing can help avoid these sorts of complications. See the table at the end of this chapter

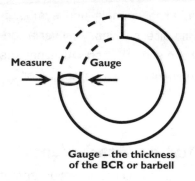

Gauge – the thickness of the BCR or barbell

for different types of piercings and suggested jewellery gauges.

Internal diameter and length

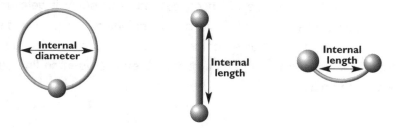

The diameter of a BCR and the length of a barbell are in essence the same thing. In the case of the BCR it is the distance between the internal edges of the ring. With a barbell it is the internal distance along the post between the two balls. What is important with these dimensions is that they should be the same length as the distance between the two piercing holes in the skin of a healed piercing.

Alternatives to beads and balls

Jewellery balls can be replaced with different shaped threaded pieces which are usually made of metal. The most common ones are cones, dumbbell weights, tusks and spikes. Others include dice, cabochons and fancy shapes that come in many designs, including animals and symbols. Beads are not so often replaced with alternatives. Any variation in a bead is usually in the size and the material used. Alternatives to metal include natural crystal, cubic zircon, wood and plastic.

Add-on attachments

An add-on attachment is something that is attached to a BCR or barbell in order to customise it. One such add-on is the shield worn with a JNB. Shields come in all shapes and sizes and can make a simple piece of jewellery look more extravagant. BCRs can also be made more fancy by fitting shaped add-ons which hang from the ring. These are often encrusted with shiny jewels and come in all sorts of shapes and sizes, including stars, animals, symbols and figures. Chains can be worn hanging down from many pieces of jewellery and, in some cases, they are used to link one piercing to another.

Other variations on the barbell

There are many variations on the barbell. Here are some popular examples.

Horseshoe or circular barbell

This takes its name from the similarity in its shape to that of a horseshoe. A barbell bent into the shape of a circle. Commonly worn in the septum, nipple and ear.

Spiral barbell

A barbell fashioned into a twisted spiral and worn in navels.

Staple barbell

A traditional barbell post with symmetrical bends at each end. The angle of the bend varies from 22.5 – 45 degrees. These are commonly used in flat skin piercings to lessen the chances of jewellery migration.

Nostril stud or screw

A barbell with a ball at one end only. The bar is then formed into a series of angled bends or curves to stop the jewellery falling out of a nose piercing.

Threaded jewellery

There are two main types: externally and internally threaded. Externally threaded is by far the most commonly manufactured type of jewellery. The end of the barbell post is threaded on the outside and the ball that fits on the end of the post is drilled and threaded on the inside. The ball then screws onto the post to form a barbell. With internally threaded jewellery, the post of the barbell is drilled out and then threaded on the inside. The ball that sits on the end of the post has a small section of threaded bar attached to it and is then screwed inside the length of the barbell post.

Types of materials used to make jewellery

Although plastic jewellery is common, metal jewellery forms the majority of all jewellery production. Jewellery is made from many types of metal, and metal alloys. An alloy is a mix of different chemical components melted down to form a new composite metal. An example of this is surgical stainless steel. Naturally, the more metals that you combine in the manufacturing process, the higher the risk of one or more of those components causing a reaction with the body.

Metal allergy

People can develop hypersensitive reactions to any metal. Nickel has been identified as one that commonly causes an allergic response when in contact with the skin.

Nickel

Where a person has become sensitised to nickel, and it comes into contact with the skin, an allergic contact dermatitis (nickel allergy) can develop. This is further exacerbated when worn inside the skin as body jewellery, particularly in an unhealed piercing. Such is the concern amongst governments in the West that many have taken action to limit the amount of nickel used in jewellery manufacture.

Am I sensitive to nickel?

If you have experienced any form of irritation from a previous piercing – such as an occasional discharge, redness or itching sensation, or a more extreme reaction where the skin peels or a burning sensation is felt – it is possible that you are sensitive to nickel. Even if you have not had a previous piercing but have had a similar reaction when wearing metal on the skin from jewellery, metal buttons, catches, clasps and studs in clothing, these are possibly also indicators of a nickel-sensitive reaction. In all cases it is safest to stay to the low-nickel options that are now available.

European Union Nickel Directive 94/27/EC

This law was adopted by the British Government in July 2001. Under the Directive the permissible levels of nickel in metal jewellery are limited to a maximum of 0.05% (500 parts of nickel per million). This means that any piece of jewellery that is to be worn in a new or unhealed piercing must comply.

A second annex of the Directive allows some jewellery with a nickel content exceeding 0.05% to be worn in healed piercings, provided that the nickel released from the jewellery is less than 0.5 microns per centimetre squared per week. It is very important to the health of a piercing that this second kind of jewellery, which includes surgical steel grade 316L, commonly used to manufacture piercing jewellery, is only worn in a healed piercing. As a rule of thumb it is safest to assume that your piercing won't have healed for at least 4–6 months. Better still, have an experienced piercing operative check out your piercing first.

Surgical stainless steel (grade 316L)

A metal with a bright silver appearance. The 'L' in 316L signifies that it has a low carbon content below 0.03%. This is probably the most widely used of all the metals in the manufacture of body jewellery. It contains 10–14 per cent nickel, way above the maximum levels recommended by European Union Nickel Directive and should not be worn in an unhealed piercing.

'Nickel-free' surgical stainless steel

This kind of steel is not totally 'nickel-free' but it guarantees that it meets the requirements of EU law in that it contains less than 0.01 per cent nickel. This jewellery is suitable for new piercings. The reason nickel is used in most metal alloys is that, in the smelting process, it bonds together all the other metals. Nickel can be replaced by other metals with similar bonding qualities, and these include chromium, molybdenum and manganese. Using these alternatives produces a much tougher finished metal which is harder to machine and, as a consequence, these pieces of jewellery are more expensive. Presently it is made only by a few highly specialist manufacturers, who each have their own specific brand name indicating that the jewellery has a low nickel content, for example Body Shock 'Nickelite'.

Titanium

Titanium is a highly suitable metal for making body piercing jewellery and it comes in various grades. It is very important for the health of your piercing that you select the highest and most suitable grade, which is as follows.

Implant grade Titanium 6A1 4V to BS7252 for implant use is the grade necessary to meet the requirements for implantation surgery, and is used for many surgical items such as heart valves and metal plates, including those used in reconstructive bone and cranial surgery.

There are lesser grades which are commonly available and which are not suitable for implant use. These include commercial grade I and II titanium which is used in general manufacture of things like motor vehicle parts and is not suitable for use in body piercing jewellery.

Another advantage of titanium is that it is easily made into bright colours of many different shades. This colour is in fact an optical illusion as a result of a trick of refracted light. It is created by applying a natural titanium oxide layer on top of the machined metal surface. The thickness of the layer determines the colour that is refracted and, because this layer is a titanium oxide, these coloured items of jewellery are as biocompatible as non-coloured titanium. Over time and with wear, these colours can fade.

Silver

Like steel, silver is an alloy and includes nickel in its composition and must meet the EU law on the nickel content. Silver is often cast into very pretty and fancy shapes which are then attached to steel posts. A common misunderstanding is that the whole of the piece of jewellery is made of silver. When silver is worn in the body it often oxidises and can turn both the jewellery and the skin black. The actual post of the barbell that passes through the skin is commonly made of surgical stainless steel and, for this reason, should not be worn in an unhealed piercing.

Gold

Gold is an alloy metal. The amount of gold each piece contains is measured in carats: for example, 9ct gold contains 9 parts gold to 15 parts other metals, and 18ctt is made up of 18 parts gold to 6 parts other metals. These other metals commonly include nickel. Pure gold is marked 24ct. To make body jewellery with a higher than 75 per cent (18ct) gold content is considered impractical. Being too soft, any threads can quickly wear out with use. Harder wearing 9ct gold is, in the main, only sold in Britain. The international standard for gold jewellery is 14ct which contains 58.4 per cent gold.

The European Union nickel law applies to gold and you should ensure that any gold piece that you are planning to purchase complies to the EU Nickel Directive.

To allow for initial swelling, most body jewellery fitted in a fresh piercing is slightly longer than the actual piercing holes. Once the piercing is healed, new jewellery generally needs to be fitted. For this reason, in most cases, it is best to use gold jewellery only in a healed piercing.

Niobium

Along with titanium, niobium is one of the most biocompatible elements on earth. The thickness of the external oxide surface film enables the creation of a vast variety of colours. It is much heavier than titanium and is more difficult to work during manufacture, generally making it more expensive than titanium.

Plated metal

A common example of plated metal is gold plating. Typically, surgical steel bars are electro-coated with thin layers of gold. Pure gold is soft and easily wears away, exposing the underlying metal.

Acrylic polymer (plastic) jewellery

Acrylic jewellery is made from polymers that are being increasingly manufactured for medical applications. These types of polymers are considered biologically inert and have proven to be remarkably stable when placed within the body. The disadvantage is that, because its surface can be microscopically porous, it requires regular cleaning. Some acrylics are not suitable for wearing inside the body and caution should be taken before buying these items.

First establish that the jewellery is suitable for wearing inside the body before purchasing it. Some jewellery suppliers and piercing operatives recommend that most kinds of acrylic jewellery only be used outside the body and should be fitted to a suitable metal barbell or BCR.

Ultraviolet sensitive acrylic 'UV'

In the daylight this jewellery looks very plain and ordinary. It comes to life in the dark environments of night clubs. When exposed to ultra violet light, its lifeless anaemic appearance is transformed into colourful glowing beacons of light. These pieces of jewellery are intended for occasional wear and should only be fitted and worn in a healed piercing. It is best to use a metal bar or stem and fit UV acrylic balls or fancy pieces to the end.

Acrylic polymer jewellery retainers

Transparent clear acrylic is sometimes used as a kind of invisible jewellery, called a retainer. The idea is that this piece is used to replace metal jewellery in obvious piercings such as the face and mouth. This is intended to appease employers, teachers and other authority figures who have a non-piercing policy. Generally they are unsatisfactory in this covert role. Most are composed of polymers that make them brittle over a period of time. Fractures can occur with excessive movement, leading to a total break.

Polytetrafluoroethylene – PTFE

Abbreviated to PTFE, this is an inert self-lubricating flexible plastic, commonly used in implantation surgery for replacement joints in hips and knees. It is popular in piercings where the likelihood of migration or rejection is high, or where people have proved sensitive to metals. It can also play an important role in piercing aftercare procedures.

Wearing jewellery

Suggested types of jewellery materials chart

To help avoid a nickel allergy, the following are suggestions as to what jewellery should be worn in a piercing.

Initial (new) piercing	Epithelisation period of an unhealed piercing	A fully healed piercing
Titanium	Titanium	Titanium
Niobium	Niobium	Niobium
PTFE	PTFE	PTFE
'Nickel-free' – gold	'Nickel-free' – gold	'Nickel-free' – gold
'Nickel-free' – steel	'Nickel-free' – steel	'Nickel-free' – steel
Except for ear piercing system studs, only the above should be used for initial piercings	This often takes at least four months – in some cases, it takes longer than a year	316L steel Acrylic and UV, etc.

Where the term 'Nickel-free' is used, it denotes that the nickel content of the metal complies with the EU Directive 94/27/EC.

Key:	Recommended jewellery materials to be worn in a new piercing and during the healing period	These should only be worn in a fully healed piercing

What to wear in an initial piercing

A piece of jewellery to be worn in a new unhealed piercing should be made of a material that can be readily sterilised and has a non-porous surface. Metal jewellery best qualifies, although PTFE can be used. If using a metal, it should be one such as titanium or niobium, as these are less likely to cause a hypersensitive skin reaction.

Plain pieces of jewellery with smooth round balls are best worn in a fresh piercing. To prevent swelling complications, the jewellery should be longer than the actual skin piercing. Do not invest in expensive pieces of jewellery until after the piercing has healed, and after it has been properly re-sized by a piercing operative. You may find smaller jewellery needs to be fitted.

Only sterilised jewellery should be fitted into any piercing, particularly an unhealed one.

Skin marking measurements and jewellery sizes for initial piercings

These suggestions are based upon accepted piercing knowledge and, personal experience, and may vary according to individual and specific circumstances. If too small a gauge of jewellery is used then there is an increased danger of it moving through the skin. This movement may cause misalignment, increased scarring and possible loss of the piercing.

Too large a gauge of jewellery requires a larger gauge needle, which can cause increased trauma to the piercing site as well as increased pain during piercing procedure. It is important to note that piercings sometimes shrink below that of the original markings, and may continue to gradually reduce over time.

Table of commonly used jewellery gauges, sizes and types

Piercing Type	Gauge (metric)	Gauge (US)	Marking Distance	Initial Jewellery Size	Jewellery Types
Eyebrow	1.2–1.6mm	14–16ga	8mm	10mm	Straight/curved barbell, BCR
Nose	1.0–1.6mm	14–18ga	as required	nostril thickness + 2–4mm	Labret stud or specialist stud
Nose	1.0–1.6mm	14–18ga	for BCR 7–10mm from edge of nostril	as above and for BCR 9–10mm	BCR or labret stud
Lip upper and lower	1.6mm	14ga	for BCR 8–10mm from edge of lip thickness + 3–4mm	BCR 10–12mm labret – lip	Labret stud or BCR
Ear lobe	1.2–1.6mm	14–16ga	symmetrical	lobe thickness +2mm	Specialist stud
Ear cartilage	1.2–1.6mm	14–16ga	must be room for BCR to reach outer edge of ear	BCR 9–12mm	BCR
Ear cartilage	1.2–1.6mm	14–16ga	ear thickness + min 2mm	6–12 mm	Labret stud or barbell
Ear tragus	1.6mm	14ga	ear thickness + min 4mm	8–12mm	labret stud, barbell or BCR
Tongue	1.6mm	14ga	tongue thickness + 8–12mm	20–26mm	Barbell
Nipple male	1.6mm	14ga	10–12mm	12–16mm	Barbell or BCR
Nipple female	1.6mm	14ga	8–20mm	12–24mm	Barbell or BCR
Navel	1.6mm	14ga	8–10mm	10–12mm	Barbell or BCR
Genital male	2.4mm	12ga	varies dependent on location	varies dependant on location	Barbell or BCR
Genital female	1.6–2.4mm	14–12ga	varies dependent on location	varies dependant on location	Barbell or BCR

Down-sizing

An example of down-sizing is replacing a 1.6mm gauge BCR with a smaller 1.2mm piece. Down-sizing in the wrong piercing can lead to complications like migration and skin rub. Below the neck, piercings should be fitted with no less than 1.6mm gauge jewellery, and any piercings below the waist on men should be fitted with a minimum of 2.4mm gauge.

Up-sizing

To up-size a piercing, the hole is stretched to fit a piece of jewellery with a larger gauge post. Some piercings, particularly genitalia, can benefit from up-sizing, as it lessens the risk of tearing the soft flesh. There are a number of specialised tapered tools that can be used to stretch a piercing. Any stretching process should be gradual; only one increment at a time should be attempted and undue force should be avoided. No bleeding or tearing of the flesh should occur. Before up-sizing, it is best to take advice from a piercing operative. Ear lobe piercings are perhaps the most dramatic example of up-sizing. A 1.2mm hole can be gradually stretched up to 20mm and above. Specially designed metal and plastic flesh tunnels are then worn.

Examples of jewellery sizes

Jewellery generally comes in the following sizes:

Gauges *(some examples)*

1.0 mm	3.0 mm	9.0 mm
1.1 mm	4.0 mm	10.0 mm
1.2 mm	5.0 mm	12.0 mm
1.6 mm	6.0 mm	15.0 mm
2.0 mm	7.0 mm	
2.4 mm	8.0 mm	

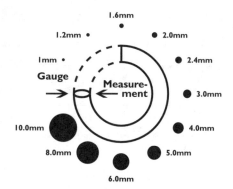

Internal dimensions

Generally, the smallest BCRs are 7mm, the largest being 32mm. The smallest barbells and labret studs are generally 5mm, with the largest being 60mm.

Chapter Five...

Things to consider
before having a piercing

Age and personal identification

IF YOU ARE UNDER the age of 21 years, or look younger, always take some form of identification with you when you have your piercing done. If you are under 16 years (in some cases under 18) in Britain, you will need to take one of your parents with you.

Personal experiences

Talk with people who have had a piercing and ask them about any problems they may have experienced, the person who pierced them and any helpful tips. Look at their piercings and be sure that is what you want on your body. Look through pictures in magazines and books for ideas.

Visit different piercing establishments. Talking with the staff and piercers is a useful way to compare standards. So that you don't forget the important questions, prepare a list of what you want to ask. The nearest piercer may not be the best one for you. The inconvenience of travelling some distance to a piercer with a good reputation should be balanced against the benefits of a safe, successful piercing.

The social consequences of body piercing

Employment prospects

Check with your employer what their policy is towards piercings. Where hygiene is important, such as in food processing, some firms have strict no-piercing policies. Likewise, jobs that involve dealing direct with the public often have restrictions on some facial piercings.

Schools and colleges

Most schools and colleges have some sort of restrictive policy on the placement of piercings. So, to avoid problems, it is wise to be up-front about any planned piercing, and always check out the school policy on body piercings beforehand. Too many children get pierced and then spend the next few weeks avoiding the head teacher or wearing a plaster over the piercing. Colleges of further education and universities generally have a less restrictive policy, but remember to check first.

Relationships

You may want to consider any impact this might have on your partner. If you are under 18 years, you really should check out the views of your parents. Often parents don't want their children to be pierced, but as body piercing becomes more socially acceptable many parents are relaxing their conservative views.

Working conditions

Consider the kind of work you do and the effect those activities might have on your piercing. An obvious one is that, if your hands are covered in grease and grime all day long, a hand web piercing is perhaps not for you. Likewise working in a dusty and dirty atmosphere is not the best environment for a facial piercing and may lead to complications. If you do a lot of bending and stretching then a navel piercing may become irritated and take longer to heal. Likewise, having a nipple piercing when you spend a lot of time lifting heavy boxes against your chest may make the piercing very tender. There are solutions: wearing padded breathable dressings may ease these potentially painful problems. Before having it done, always consider the implications your normal daily routine could have for your piercing. Talk through any concerns with a piercing operative as well as anyone you know with a similar piercing.

Sports and physical training

Don't have a piercing done in the afternoon and expect to be able to play a physical sport the same evening. It is advisable to leave a gap of a few days between having your piercing done and any sporting activity. Avoid putting stress on the wound by excessive impact and stretching. Think about possible protective dressings that you can wear and purchase them in advance of your piercing. Excessive perspiration can be a problem to a piercing wound. Likewise, swimming without a protective waterproof dressing can lead to an increased risk of a piercing infection.

Swelling and healing

The more you find out about the piercing you are planning, the less likely you are to experience problems. One aspect of a piercing that often surprises people is the length of time it takes for a piercing to heal properly. Special care will need to be taken when bathing for the first month or so. Some localised skin trauma should be expected. The extent of the swelling varies between individuals, and depends on the area pierced as well as the technique used by the piercer. Some swelling will be immediately apparent with all piercings, and often increases over the following few days, lasting from a few days, to several weeks.

Your current state of health

If you are suffering from an illness or are taking medication, their effect upon the healing process of your piercing, as well the impact of your piercing upon any medical condition, should be considered very carefully. For haemophiliacs a piercing could prove fatal, and relatively minor conditions, such as eczema, can lead to painful complications, especially if they are close to the piercing. You should always declare any medical condition to your piercing operative prior to the piercing. This may not necessarily prevent you from having a piercing, but it will enable any special needs to be provided for, and prevent any potentially serious complications.

The following is a list, although not an exhaustive one, of some conditions that should be investigated and declared to the piercing operative before you are pierced.

Allergic reactions – If you suffer from a nickel allergy, avoid any jewellery that has nickel in it. If you are allergic to adhesive plasters, tell your piercer so that he or she doesn't put a plaster dressing on after the piercing. Likewise, any other allergic re-action that might be brought on by the piercing procedure should be reported beforehand.

Asthma – People often get anxious prior to a piercing. For an asthmatic, this stress could bring on an attack. Have any medica-tion with you during the piercing. With an oral piercing, consider that, if the jewellery becomes detached and enters the lung, this could trigger a potentially fatal asthma attack. Regularly tighten balls on oral jewellery to help prevent this happening.

Cellulitis – This condition can lead to septicaemia. Talk to your doctor first.

Diabetes – Check with your GP. In particular check if healing will be inhibited after the piercing.

Fainting – If you are prone to fainting, have someone with you during the piercing and for at least four hours afterwards. Don't have a piercing on an empty stomach. Eat something within four hours of a piercing, preferably no later than an hour before your appointment.

Genital warts – They should only be considered if they affect the area relevant to the piercing requested. These should then be discussed with your GP prior to piercing.

Haemorrhagic *(bleeding)* – Disorders including leukaemia. A piercing could be potentially fatal.

Heart disease – Discuss your intention to be pierced with your medical consultant; you will need their written permission before you can be pierced. A new piercing, even an ear lobe, poses an increased risk to the body from infections. If you have had a heart valve fitted, you run the risk of a bacterial infection of the heart called endocarditis.

HIV/AIDS – Take advice from your GP and talk this one through with the piercer.

Keloids – If you already suffer from keloid scarring, there is a high risk that your piercing will develop further keloid complications.

Other conditions – Illness can affect your body's ability to heal. If you are unwell, don't get pierced. Some cancer and immuno-suppressant drugs can increase the risk of endocarditis.

Rheumatic fever – It is possible with rheumatic fever to sustain damage to the heart valves. If damage has occurred, there is a risk of infective endocarditis.

Seizures *(e.g. epilepsy)* – Again, check with your medical practitioner. Provided you are up to date with your medication, it is possible to be pierced.

Skin conditions – Piercing should not be performed on skin that is diseased or affected by a rash, psoriasis, eczema or moles. If it affects the area or is likely to affect the area being pierced, it is probably best not to be pierced. Talk to your GP or skin specialist.

Other things to consider

Alcohol, social drugs or other substances – You should not be pierced whilst under the influence of any substance, including alcohol, nor should you take any drugs, other than those prescribed by your doctor, 24 hours before a piercing and 72 hours afterwards.

Blood poisoning *(septicaemia)* – A percentage of piercings do become infected. A reputable piercing operative will have in place very effective infection control procedures. These make the chances of the piercing becoming infected during the procedure very remote. A piercing is most at risk from infection during the healing period after piercing. It is very important to plan your post-piercing aftercare routine beforehand. If you think that your piercing has become infected, you should seek immediate advice from a piercing operative and/or a doctor.

Body size and shape – Some idiosyncrasies of body design may affect the chances of having a successful piercing – for example, 'outie' navels and tied tongues.

Breast implants – If you have breast implants, because of the increased risk of infection and complications, you should not undertake a piercing of the breast without first consulting your cosmetic surgeon.

Changing your mind once you are pierced – Removing piercing jewellery and allowing the piercing to heal over is going to leave a scar. How noticeable that scar will be depends upon a number of factors: the location on your body, how long the piercing has been in place, how well it has healed and whether or not complications have occurred.

Chemotherapy – This treatment affects your body's ability to heal itself, increasing the risk of infection. It is best not to have a piercing whilst undergoing this treatment.

Don't rush into a body piercing – Give some thought as to the kind of piercing you prefer. Read the other sections in this book and put the information into practice before finally deciding to have the piercing done.

Going away on holiday – Give yourself a cushion of at least two weeks before going on holiday to let your piercing start to heal, particularly if going abroad.

Hospitalisation – Most medical procedures, including x-rays, require the removal of any body jewellery in and around the area to be treated. Removing jewellery always runs the risk of the piercing closing up. How quickly this will happen depends on the length of time since piercing and the condition and state of the piercing. If you have a planned medical procedure due within six months of having a piercing, discuss this with your medical consultant.

Menstruation – Prior to menstruating, some women can experience fluid retention which leads to an increase in size, particularly around the abdomen. This can have an effect on an unhealed piercing. Inform your piercer so that he or she can take this into account when calculating the piercing dimension.

Mobile piercers – In order to maintain high standards of hygiene and maintain disease control, piercing needs to be carried out in a controlled environment. A domestic lounge or a kitchen don't meet the necessary hygiene requirements. Unless a specialist mobile piercing unit is provided, this kind of service can be a health risk.

Pain – Pain is a very subjective and individual experience. Everyone feels pain differently. Some people feel having a piercing is painful, whilst others don't. Millions of people are pierced each year and consider the level of pain a worthwhile trade-off for the other benefits. You should consider your own attitude to pain and discuss any fears with people that have piercings.

Based upon my observations of the reactions, as well as the comments of people just after being pierced, I have prepared a sliding scale of pain experienced in piercings. This has number 1 as the most painful and 14 as the least. Remember, this is only a rough guide and everyone has their own unique translation of pain.

1. Nose – septum	6. Lip	11. Tongue
2. Nose – bridge	7. Nose – nostril	12. Top ear
3. Male nipple	8. Eyebrow	13. Navel
4. Ear – tragus	9. Male genitalia	14. Ear lobe
5. Female nipple	10. Female genitalia	

Other matters to consider before being pierced

Paperwork – You will be expected to fill out some paperwork which will include your full name, address and telephone number, and your date of birth. As well as answering a series of medical questions, you will be asked to sign a consent and disclaimer form before being pierced. A second form is usually signed after the piercing, stating your satisfaction with the procedure. If you suffer from an illness, or are on medication, then you might be asked to provide a letter from your doctor, confirming that the piercing won't interfere with these.

Piercings abroad – Some parts of the world may not maintain the same high standards of hygiene as in Britain. Special care is needed to maintain a healthy piercing. Even in countries like the USA, where similar standards of hygiene exist, it is still not a good idea to have a piercing carried out whilst on holiday.

Pregnancy – Pregnant and nursing mothers should consult their midwife or medical consultant for advice. Any piercing carries a risk of infection, and the effect of any drugs that might be needed in its treatment should be considered.

Take a friend – Where possible, have someone with you for moral support. Your friend will probably remember more about any special instructions the piercing operative gives you on how to look after your piercing. They may also be better able to ask the questions that you want answered.

Chapter Six...

How to spot a reputable body piercer

Y OU WILL HAVE a good idea that you have arrived at a reputable piercing establishment by the way you are treated. The piercing operative will be pleased to show you around, explaining what the equipment is for, how it works, and answering your questions. They will happily discuss your concerns and make you aware of the risks involved in piercing. The piercing operative should have a sound knowledge of post-piercing aftercare and how to reduce any risks. Clients will be expected to return at intervals after piercing for check-ups.

To help you find the right piercing operative and make your decision, here are some of the things that you should expect of a reputable piercing operative.

Local Authority Environmental Health Department

In London most of the boroughs have adopted the Local Authorities Act 1991, and do license the body piercing premises. Outside London some local authorities run approved body piercer schemes. Under the scheme, piercers agree to abide by an approved code of conduct. By contacting your local Environmental Health Department you should be able to obtain a list of particip-ating piercers.

Reputation

A good way of finding a piercing operative is through recommendation from someone who has had a satisfactory piercing. This doesn't necessarily mean that the piercer is the one for you. Check them out against the points raised in this section before deciding to be pierced.

Qualifications and experience

Ask to see certificates for any qualifications that they may hold. Find out what experience they have of body piercing and, in particular, their experience in carrying out the kind of piercing that you want done.

Pre-piercing consultation and information

You should make an effort to speak with the piercer prior to having a piercing, in order to discuss any concerns. At the same time you should disclose any medical information that may be relevant to the piercing procedure. This information should always be treated by the piercing operative in absolute confidence.

It is essential that body piercing operatives have a clear understanding of good practice and that they put this into effect. In order to achieve this, and comply with various requirements under the Health and Safety at Work Act 1974 and regulations made thereunder, it is necessary for a written method statement to be prepared. Ask to see a copy of this statement.

First aid

The piercing operative or an employee should hold a current HSE-approved basic first aid qualification. A responsible piercing operative will want to ensure that they are able to cope with medical emergencies.

The piercer should be vaccinated against the Hepatitis B virus and should not be under the influence of drugs, alcohol or other substances.

Records and forms

Displayed on the premises should be a list of piercings along with their current price. Written information explaining the possible risks involved in body piercing, as well as detailed post-piercing aftercare instructions, should be available. Any piercing operative should keep a written record for a period of at least three years of all the people that they have pierced. Sterilising equipment should be properly checked and maintained, and records kept. Don't be afraid to ask to see them.

Age policy

Other than by voluntary agreement, and with the exception of genital piercings, there is no legal lower age limit on being pierced. A reputable piercer will have a piercing age policy, and most will not pierce anyone under 16 years without the express consent of their parents.

Premises

You can tell a lot about a piercer by their premises. If the reception is dirty and untidy, this may be an indicator of other potential problems hidden behind the scenes.

The piercing room

Privacy is very important where a piercing is going to take place. The actual piercing room must be separate from other activities and in circumstances where privacy can be assured. The piercing area should be well illuminated, with heating and ventilation, and be large enough to provide adequate space for the piercing activities to be performed safely and efficiently.

Hygiene and infection control

All surfaces in the piercing room must be clean and capable of being readily cleansed and disinfected. The piercing chair or couch must be made of a washable material and then covered with a clean disposable paper sheet for each client. There must be suitable hand washing facilities with hot and cold running water, together with soap and paper towels or other suitable means of hand drying. Anyone working in the piercing room should be wearing clean clothing; ideally they should wear a plastic one-use apron. A new one should be used for every client.

Equipment

Separate suitable washing facilities with hot and cold running water should be provided, in order that any instruments used in the body piercing procedure can be cleaned. An ultrasonic cleaner and autoclave steriliser will both be used as part of the instrument cleaning process. Without a suitable autoclave the instruments and jewellery can't be properly sterilised on the premises. The "clean" and "dirty" areas must be separate and the flow of operations should ensure that cross-contamination does not occur. There must be no smoking or eating in the piercing room, and a suitable first aid kit must be readily available.

Jewellery

There should be a very wide selection of jewellery to suit different types of piercings, as well as a range available for down-sizing after the piercing has been done. Advice should be given on the different types of jewellery that can be worn in new and healed piercings.

Post-piercing
aftercare instructions

Both verbal and written instructions should be issued to every client that has a piercing. These should include cleaning instructions, information on how to identify potential problems, how they can be avoided, and the control of any blood loss. You should make a point of reading this information before you have a piercing.

Post-piercing check-ups

Any reputable piercing operative will definitely want to see you after your piercing for at least one post-piercing check-up.

Chapter Seven...

What happens during a piercing?

WHEN DECIDING TO have a piercing it is very helpful to know what to expect. The information you have beforehand will enable you to make a safe choice. This section covers most aspects of a piercing procedure, from filling out paperwork to what to wear.

Choosing jewellery

All jewellery used for piercing must be of a suitable grade titanium, niobium, low-nickel stainless steel, or dense low porosity plastic. Any jewellery to be fitted into a piercing must be properly sterilised.

Hygiene

The room, the piercing operative and their clothes should all be clean. The chair or couch that is used should have a washable surface. Either tissue roll should be placed over it and changed after each customer, or the surface should be cleaned down with a disinfectant spray between customers.

Hand washing and latex gloves

You should see the piercing operative wash their hands in front of you. A new pair of latex gloves should then be worn and these should be changed every time the piercing operative's hands make contact with work surfaces, the floor, cabinet door handles, etc. In order to minimise the risk of cross-contamination of micro-organisms between objects and the customer, it is normal for a piercing operative to change their gloves several times during a single piercing procedure.

What to wear

Depending on the location of the piercing, you may be asked to partially undress. It is always a good idea to consider the type of clothing you are going to wear. With a navel piercing your under-wear will probably be on show, so wear your best pair!

Preparing the area of skin to be pierced

For facial and ear piercing, it is best to wash your hair before the piercing appointment. Take time to wash the skin around the piercing site. Ears should be thoroughly cleaned and any facial make-up removed. For a nose piercing, blow your nose and clear away any dried mucus that may be lying inside your nostrils. With genital piercings, wash the site to be pierced and surrounding area just before your appointment. Even though you have washed the area, expect your piercing operative to clean it again with an alcohol-based solution prior to piercing.

Marking the piercing

Every piercing should be measured and marked, even tongue piercings.

Check the markings

Once the area has been marked, you should be given the opportunity to view it through a mirror and agree the location.

Forceps clamps

These are used to minimise the contact around the piercing site during the procedure. Clamps bring the two marked piercing points into line and help to reduce the thickness of skin. This enables the needle to travel in a straight line through the skin in the correct position. The clamps should be applied with gentle pressure, avoiding unnecessary discomfort and minimising the chance of bruising.

The needle

There are two distinct methods of piercing. Both use pre-sterilised hollow needles. One type of needle carries a plastic sheath called a cannula, and the other doesn't. The one without the cannula is called a blade. With either method, by ensuring that the packet seal is unbroken before it is used, the needle can be checked for single use and sterility. After use, it should be put into a special used-needle container, called a sharps bin.

Fitting the jewellery

Depending on which method is used, the jewellery to be fitted is either placed into one end of the plastic cannula tube or the back of the blade. The jewellery is then very carefully and painlessly fed through the piercing by guiding the plastic tube or blade through the skin. The ball or bead is then fitted to complete the piercing.

Bleeding

Approximately half the people pierced show some signs of bleeding. If your piercing bleeds, your piercing operative will want to stem any bleeding before you leave the premises.

Recovery

Everyone needs a few minutes to re-gather their composure. Sometimes a sugar lolly is given to help speed recovery.

Checking that you are happy with your piercing

Again you should view your piercing through a mirror. If you have any concerns about the piercing location or alignment, you should tell the piercing operative at this time.

Applying a dressing

Where appropriate, a clean breathable dressing will then be applied. If you are allergic to plaster adhesive, remember to tell your piercing operative before a dressing is applied.

Aftercare instructions

The piercing operative should then inform you of all the pertinent aftercare points in relation to the piercing. These should also be put in writing for you to take away and read. Take time to understand them and ask any questions.

Check-up appointment

To ensure that your piercing is healing properly, your piercing operative should make an appointment with you for an aftercare check-up.

Fainting or lightheadedness

It is normal for people to suffer pre-piercing anxiety. Sometimes, after the piercing has been completed and you begin to relax, a feeling of lightheadedness, or a dizzy sensation, is experienced and, in extreme cases, fainting.

Anaesthetics

In Britain a local anaesthetic injection can only be administered by a registered medical practitioner. The issue of using topical surface anaesthetics in body piercing is currently subject to major debate. Three types of anaesthetics are used in body piercing practices:

Ethyl chloride

A clear liquid spray, with potential side effects, including frost bite, as well as the danger of being accidentally sprayed in the eyes, inner ear and onto mucous membrane.

Xylocaine

A clear liquid spray that can have severe adverse effects on the body's respiration, central nervous and cardiovascular systems. Severe reactions can lead to the body suffering anaphylactic shock. When used on the tongue there is a serious danger of asphyxiation.

Emla cream

A drug that is meant only to be prescribed by a doctor. Skin numbing only occurs after one hour.

If a body piercing operative chooses to offer you an anaesthetic, a separate questionnaire should be completed to ascertain any possible allergic reactions to its use.

Considering that a piercing is such a very short (typically 1–3 seconds) procedure, most body piercers and medical professionals share the view that the dangers in using anaesthetics are greater than the benefits. It is like having an anaesthetic before having an injection in the arm.

Paperwork

Expect to fill out your personal details on a form. Example, your name, address and age, etc. As well as any relevant medical conditions that you may be suffering from and medication that you may be taking. Usually, when you sign the form, you will be consenting to the piercing procedure. After the piercing you may be asked to sign a form stating your satisfaction with the piercing.

Chapter Eight...

Types of piercings

S ET OUT HERE are over 50 different types of piercings, each
has a detailed description and in some cases an illustration.
The piercings are divided into six sections. Accompanying the
piercings is supplementary information about the history of the
piercing, a description and location of the piercing, the piercing
procedure, effects of swelling, healing times, types of suitable
jewellery, some common complications and how to avoid them.

Facial piercings

Eyes ...

Eyebrow

History: Around 1250BC the Phoenicians were great seafarers
who flourished along the eastern shores of the Mediterranean.
Based in the city of Tyre, their skills included the manufacture
of gold jewellery embellished with coloured glass beads. They are
reputed to have worn an eyebrow piercing as a sign of status.
Later, this practice spread to Africa when they colonised Morocco
and Tunisia.

Description and Location

Positioned on either right or left eyebrow, the preferred location
is just above the outer corner of the eye and at a slight angle,

so that the jewellery flows with the curve of the eyebrow. Piercing the eyebrow towards the nose should be avoided, as there is a danger of damage to one of the facial supra-orbital nerves. Piercing this nerve can cause partial muscle paralysis of the face.

Procedure

Before the piercing appointment any face make-up should be removed around the area of the piercing. Normally you will be seated for this piercing, although it can be done with you lying on your back. The skin around the area to be pierced will be cleaned and marked with a special skin marking pen. Through the use of a mirror  you should agree jointly with your piercing operative the exact placement of the jewellery. Expect some initial bleeding that normally stops within a few minutes.

Swelling

Sometimes swelling occurs quickly, and can remain for a week or longer. Occasionally some temporary bruising can occur on the top eye lid, giving the appearance of a black eye.

Healing Time

Four to five months, although in some cases this can take longer.

Types of Suitable Jewellery

BCR, barbell straight or curved
(minimum 1.2–1.6mm maximum gauge).

Extra Care Considerations

Eyebrow piercings have perhaps the highest tendency to migrate. Extra care should be taken, therefore, not to disturb the piercing during the first four months.

Nose . . .

History: Nose piercing has been practised for thousands of years by the Beja and Bedouin nomadic tribes of the Middle East, where nose rings are a sign of status and are given as a gift from the husband to his wife on their wedding day. Early records date nose piercing as far back as 2000BC. These are references in the Bible, in Genesis 24:22, where Abraham gives a wedding gift of a nose ring to one of his newly wedded daughters-in-law.

The practice was taken to India by the Moghal ruler Akbar in 1526, and is still popularly maintained. Today in India a nose piercing is seen as a symbol of beauty. It is generally worn on the left side of the nose for medicinal purposes, and is believed to relieve menstrual cramps and to ease labour during childbirth. At special gatherings and festivals this piercing is often enhanced by the wearing of a chain linking the piercing to the ears or, in some regions of India, linking both nostrils. During the 1960s, people travelled to India from the West, bringing the practice back with them. Nose piercings then became an integral fashion accessory associated with the hippy movement.

Nostril (side of nose)

Description and Location

Located on either side of the nose, usually in the small skin crease just above the nostril curve, it is sometimes called the 'Ala' after the medical term for this part of the anatomy. Studs are most commonly worn, although wearing a BCR is becoming increasingly popular.

Procedure

Just before being pierced clear your nostrils of any mucus and remove any make-up. The nose will be cleaned on the outside with alcohol and saline solution on the inside. The position will be marked and should be agreed by you before the piercing takes place. Small specialist clamps will be gently applied and the nose then pierced.

Swelling

Some redness and swelling around the piercing on the outside of the nose is to be expected. This should reduce quickly, and usually disappears within two weeks. The swelling is normally greatest on the inner nostril, forming a small cone shaped swelling which takes several weeks to reduce.

Healing Times
A minimum of four months

Types of Suitable Jewellery

Although 1.0mm and 1.2mm gauge jewellery is commonly fitted, there is strong scientific evidence to indicate that cartilage piercings heal with fewer complications when larger 1.6mm gauge jewellery is fitted.

When a conventional straight ear piercing stud is used in an initial piercing, the stud is prone to being accidentally knocked. **A labret stud does not suffer these problems as the flat plate keeps the stud secure inside the nostril**. Special labret studs with tiny jewelled balls are made especially for this purpose.

Extra Care Considerations

Despite the poor location of the piercing next to often infected discharging mucus, nostril piercings in the main have a surprisingly high success rate, although problems can occur, particularly if a streaming cold is contracted shortly after the piercing.

Spring Trigger Piercing Systems – 'Guns'

The common practice of using an ear piercing system in the nose poses a number of serious dangers, including disease transmission as well as possible damage to the nose cartilage. Unless the 'gun' manufacturer's instructions specifically state that it's safe to use the system on the nose, the nose should not be pierced by use of a 'gun'.

Septum
Description and Location
The septum is the flange of skin-covered cartilage located centrally at the base of the nose, where it joins the upper lip, forming a partition to create two nostrils. Typically, the piercing is placed nearer to the end of the nose rather than in the centre of the septum.

If you are looking for something unusual, this could be it, but note it is considered a more painful piercing than most. The piercing should form a horizontal line across the septum and is carried out in much the same way as the nostril piercing.

Healing Times
Minimum of four months.

Swelling
Expect some swelling in the first few days, but this should reduce within a week or so.

Types of Suitable Jewellery
Minimum 1.6mm gauge BCRs and barbells can be worn. Specially designed, horseshoe shaped retainers are made for a less obtrusive appearance. When the piercing has healed, spike and horn extensions can be worn for effect on a barbell.

Extra Care Considerations
The end of the nose will be tender for several days and care should be taken when wiping or blowing the nose. For people who suffer from regular running noses, this piercing may prove troublesome.

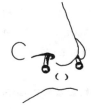

Bridge (Erl)

Description and Location

This is located between the eyes in the soft fold of skin at the bridge of the nose. A person named Erl once had a nose bridge piercing and the name has stuck, with this piercing commonly being referred to by his name.

Procedure

The procedure is much the same as that for the nostril and septum piercings. The horizontal alignment in a bridge piercing is even more critical than in a septum piercing. If the positioning is at a slight angle the effect will be spoiled.

Swelling

The initial swelling can be severe, often with some surface bruising which gradually reduces, return- ing to normal after 2–3 weeks.

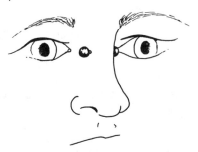

Healing Time

Minimum four months. Each individual is different and it can in some cases take over a year.

Types of Suitable Jewellery

The jewellery should be a minimum of 1.6mm gauge. Straight or curved barbells are most commonly worn, although BCRs can be fitted. After the piercing has healed, barbells are often customised by adding either coloured or jewelled balls. Spikes and horns extend the length of the barbell, accentuating the piercing.

Extra Care Considerations

The chances of jewellery rejection are quite high compared with the norm for most types of piercings. Any rejection scar in this location is likely to be obvious. Therefore a piercing that is migrat- ing is best removed before it totally rejects.

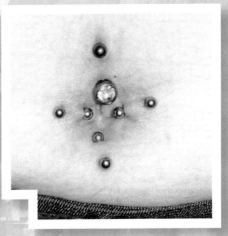

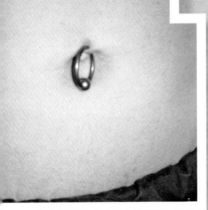

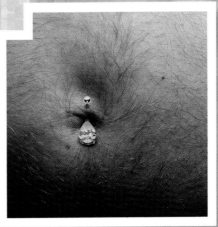

navel (bellybutton) is probably the
ost popular piercing after ear lobes.
sorts of people - tall, short, thin, fat,
ung and old have piercings.
en as well as women have navel
ercings. Multiple navel piercings are
ss common. They can take longer to
al, but they are very striking.

**jewelled
spiral barbell**

jewelled duo BCR

jewelled BCR

**UV Spiky flower
navel bar**

NAVEL piercings

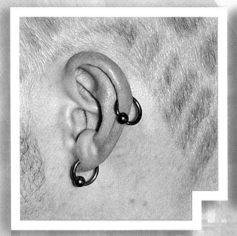

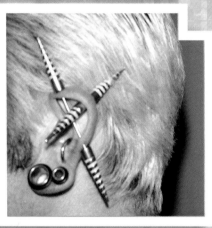
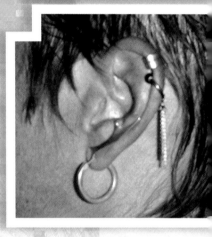

fircones labret stud

flesh tunnels

faceted jewelled balls

circular barbells

*Most parts of the ears can b
pierced, and over 12 different type
of ear piercings are described in th
book. Standard lobe piercings ca
gradually be stretched up to muc
larger sizes, and flesh tunnels fitted
Ear piercings can be designed to b
simple or in some cases mor
extravagant. Labret studs can ofte
bring comfort to a troublesom
piercing.
Jewelled balls can be added to
plain Labret Stud.*

EAR piercings

Sponsored by Body Shock

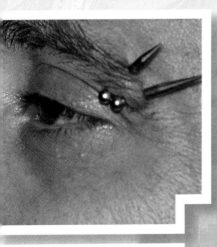

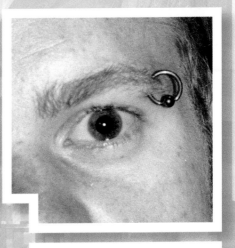

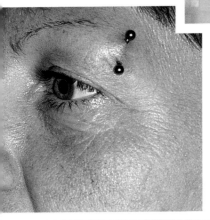

acial piercings are more noticeable, o if you are considering a facial iercing, consider their impact on amily, friends and employers. Eyebrow piercings often have an igher incidence of jewellery ejection. If this happens, a ermanent scar can remain.

silver trident eyebrow barbell

curved barbells

cones are used to customised barbells

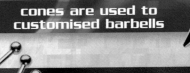

UV eyebrow balls

EYEBROW piercings

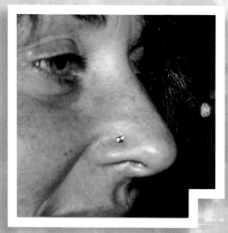
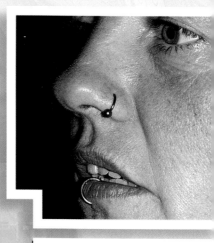
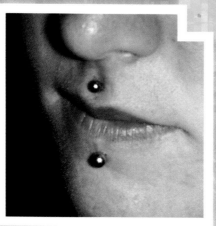
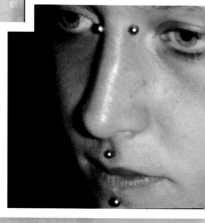

segment rings

**jewelled balls
(faceted stones)**

jewelled nose studs

facial spikes

Both studs and BCR's are suitable fo
wearing in a nose piercing; like othe
piercings on the face they can have
big impact on other people.
Specially designed nose studs, with
bent or curved post, help keep th
jewellery in place.
Segment rings are ideal where
clean uninterrupted line is desired.

NOSE & LIP piercings

Sponsored by Body Shock

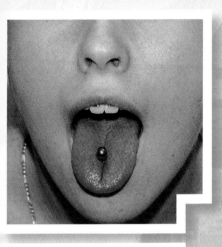
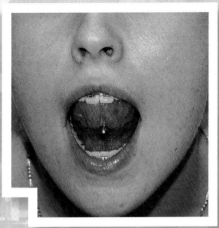

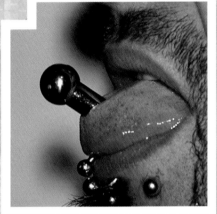

A barbell passes vertically through the tongue, with balls top and bottom to keep it in place. Some people stretch their piercing and fit large gauge jewellery.

To help prevent damage to teeth and gums, correctly sized jewellery should be fitted and like all piercing jewellery, this should be checked at regular intervals – at least twice yearly.

barbells

glow in the dark novelties

jewelled balls tiffany

novelty balls

TONGUE piercings

Sponsored by Body Shock

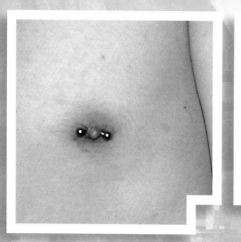

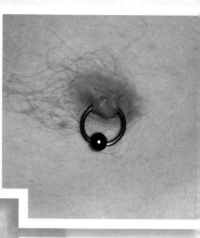

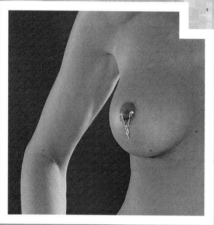

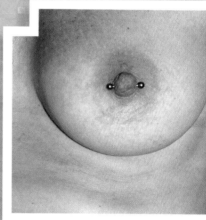

Jewelled heart closure ring

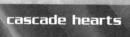

cascade hearts

silver bullet

nipple rounders

Both men and women enjoy wearin a nipple piercing. They are mos commonly pierced horizontally. Initic jewellery will become loose after onl a few weeks, and will need replacin with properly fitted jewellery.

This prevents them being caught o tugged accidentally, when dressing o lifting heavy objects.

NIPPLE piercings

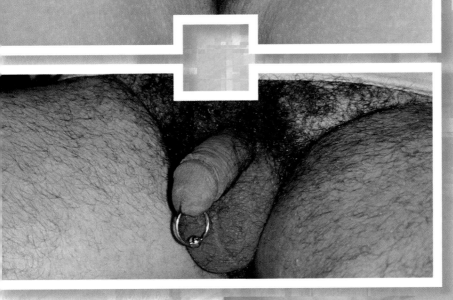

Although these piercings are very popular, they are the kind of piercing that is seen the least. However, when conversation turns to body piercing, these are the kinds of piercings that provoke most interest.

For comfort and safety, it is sometimes helpful to 'upsize' jewellery to a larger gauge.

Ordinary every day people have piercings which only their closest friends know about.

ram's head closure ring

curved (navel) barbell

large gauge BCR

BCR with ball

INTIMATE piercings

Sponsored by Body Shock

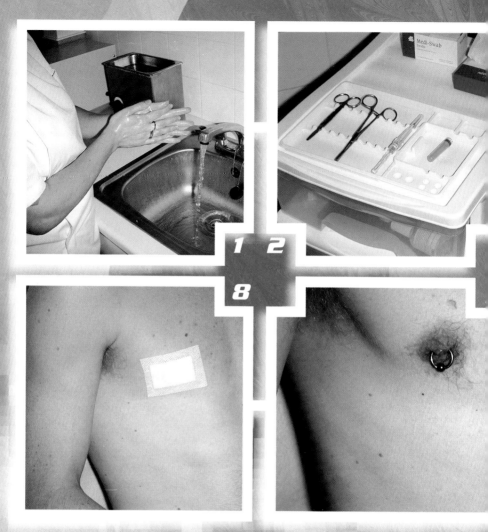

READ SEQUENCE LEFT TO RIGHT ON TOP LINE

STEP 1- Hand washing is vital for good hygiene.

STEP 2- All instruments must be properly sterilised in an autoclave.

STEP 3- The area of skin to be pierced should first be cleaned. Then to ensure that the jewellery is in the right place and fits comfortably, the skin must be measured and marked.

STEP 4- A small fold of skin is gently pinched in a pair of forcep clamps during the piercing.

A TYPICA

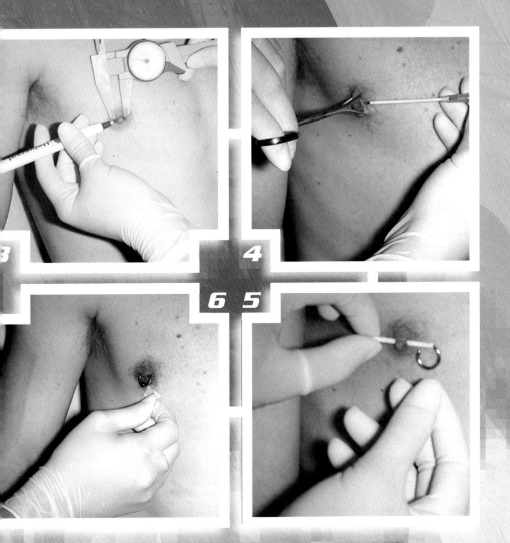

SEQUENCE CONTINUES RIGHT TO LEFT ON BOTTOM LINE.
STEP 5- The jewellery is guided painlessly through the skin.
STEP 6- Some piercings bleed a little for a few minutes after piercing.
STEP 7- A bead secures the BCR in place.
STEP 8- Wearing a dressing for the first few hours after having a piercing prevents staining to clothes and helps maintain comfort.

ROCEDURE

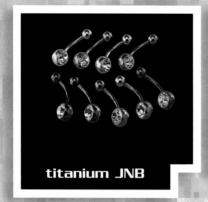

titanium JNB

silver crown with steel stem

9&18ct gold dolphin

a navel piercing

star shield silver & steel

millennium/steel

fuschia/steel

quadraphenia 9&18ct gold

Jewelled Navel Barbells (JNBs) are made from Titanium, Gold, Silver, other metals and Plastic. Navel piercings can be prone to catching the waist band of clothing, therefore more extravagant pieces are best worn for occasional use. For every day wear, a correctly fitted simple piece is usually most comfortable.

JNB jewelled navel bar

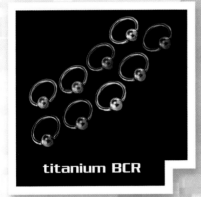

titanium BCR

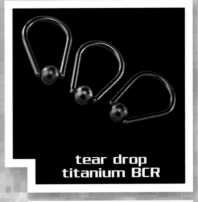

**tear drop
titanium BCR**

**heavy gauge chunk
ring in steel**

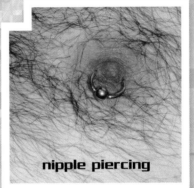

nipple piercing

Plain BCR's (rings) can be made more interesting by fitting coloured beads and specially designed inserts. They come in many different shapes and sizes, and can be worn in most piercing locations.

They vary in size from very fine (1.2mm gauge) to heavy metal chuck rings (sometimes 20mm gauge).

'D' BCR

**black jack
titanium BCR**

double BCR

segment rings

BCR ball closure rings

titanium barbells

titanium spiral barbells

9&18ct gold dumbbells

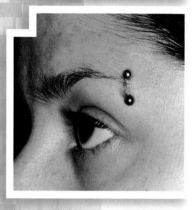

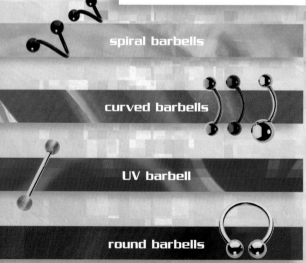

spiral barbells

curved barbells

UV barbell

round barbells

Barbells can be straight, curved or twisted into a spiral. The plain balls can be replaced with novel shaped pieces such as dumbbells, or cast into an unusual shape. Barbells can be worn in most piercing locations.

BARBELL jewellery

Jewellery supplied courtesy of Body Shock

**titanium
labret studs**

titanium spikes

**9&18ct gold
jewelled labret**

**labret studs
for comfort**

*The flat plate at the back of a
labret stud makes wearing
jewellery though the lips and
ears more comfortable.*

*They can also be worn in a
nostril piercing, which helps
prevent against accidental
removal.*

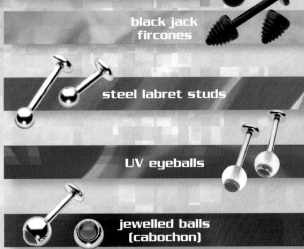

**black jack
fircones**

steel labret studs

UV eyeballs

**jewelled balls
(cabochon)**

LABRET studs

Jewellery supplied courtesy of Body Shock

**tri-celtic
nipple shield**

**nipple barbell with
hanging lady add-on**

**jewelled navel bar with
a spider's web add-on**

frog closure ring

**silver jewelled
swirly dropper**

jewelled quad drops

silver vampire add-on

**9&18ct
daisy chain**

Barbells and BCRs can be customised by fitting specially designed add-ons. The choices are extensive, ranging from a simple chain dangling from a barbell, to an extravagantly designed nipple shield. Standard jewelled navel barbells are often customised with silver and gold add-ons.

JEWELLERY ADD-ONS

UV two-piece septum spikes

jewelled UV balls can be added to existing jewellery

UV BCR

UV flesh tunnels

Ultra violet jewellery is the trendiest form of jewellery for those who enjoy clubbing. Night club dance floor lights bring UV jewellery to life. UV is best worn with a metal barbell or labret stud.

UV balls and other novelty items can be added to existing jewellery for added attraction.

UV threaded spiky flower

items to add to a tongue barbell

UV facial spikes

UV navel bar

ULTRA VIOLET JEWELLERY

Jewellery supplied courtesy of Body Shock

CUSTOMISED

replacement novelty balls

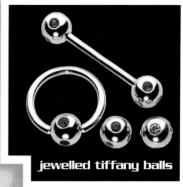

jewelled tiffany balls

stirrups, can be added to a barbell

BCR's are easily customised using jewelled beads

jewelled duo BCR

jewelled asteroid can be added

screw barbell

dolphin chain, can customise barbells & BCRs

A plain piece of body jewellery can be cheaply and effectively customised. Simply replace the plain metal ball with a jewelled one. Specialist pieces are designed for specific piercings, such as eyebrows and navels.

CUSTOMISED jewellery

Third Eye

A variation of the bridge piercing. Instead of being horizontally pierced between the eyes, the third eye is instead pierced vertically, central to the face and upwards towards the forehead. In Eastern cultures the chakra located in the middle of the forehead is regarded as the mind's eye. When opened it is believed that one can see into the higher spiritual realms. Chances of jewellery rejection are even higher than with a conventional bridge piercing. The procedure and considerations are similar to those for the bridge and minimum 1.6mm gauge jewellery should be fitted – usually a flat skin staple or curved barbell.

Mouth ... (oral piercings)

History: Piercing the tongue was regarded first by the Mayans of around 700BC and, later, the Aztec civilisations of Central America, as a highly spiritual practice, and was reserved only for high priests and royalty. When, in 1521, the Spanish conquistadors arrived on the American continent, they virtually wiped out both the Aztec people and their practice of tongue piercing.

The first report of a tongue piercing in western medical literature appears in 1992. The emergence of tongue piercing in modern times has deep sexual connotations, as do many piercings. The tongue piercing is believed to increase sexual gratification during oral sex. However it should be added, as the popularity of this piercing has broadened into mainstream society, this sexual significance has been diluted. It has given way to the desire to be seen to be cool.

Lip piercing has been practised for thousands of years and continues in many parts of the world even today. Men of the African Makololo tribe insert wooden plugs into the lips of women as signs of their ownership and it is seen by the members of the tribe as a sign of great beauty.

Procedure

Before the appointment any facial hair and make-up in the area of the piercing should be removed. Seating is usually in an upright posture. With both tongue and lip piercings, small amounts of saliva can dribble from the mouth. To avoid it getting onto clothing a disposable or washable bib is provided. A mouthwash solution is used to rinse before and after the piercing. The outside skin of the lip, after being cleaned with a medical wipe, will be marked for location. For tongue piercings, the top surface of the tongue should be dried before marking. To ensure that the needle doesn't make contact with the teeth and gums, clamps will be used to hold the tongue or lip in a safe position. Expect some bleeding – the amount varies between individuals and normally stops within a few minutes.

Swelling

The extent of the swelling varies between individuals and there is no way to determine in advance who will experience most swelling. Generally the worst swelling peaks after three or four days. Placing ice cubes in the mouth and holding them behind the piercing can help keep the swelling under control. There are a number of things that you can do to limit the swelling and potential discomfort, and these are set out in chapter 9, 'How to care for a piercing'.

Anaesthetics

Using anaesthetic on the tongue can be extremely dangerous. The tongue is a muscle and, when anaesthetised, a relaxed tongue can easily move uncontrolled into a position where it blocks the airway. In such a case there would be a serious danger of asphyxiation. Another concern is that an ingredient contained within the anaesthetic might trigger anaphylactic shock.

Tongue

Description and Location

A tongue piercing is usually fitted with a long barbell which passes through the tongue vertically from top to bottom, through the centre of the tongue. To avoid cutting through the fraenum, it is positioned slightly to one side underneath the tongue.

Types of Suitable Jewellery

A barbell of minimum 1.6mm gauge is fitted in the initial piercing. It must have a generous amount of spare length to allow for any amount of swelling. It is advisable to return to the piercing operative between 7–21 days after the piercing in order to have the barbell shortened, returning again at regular intervals to have progressively shorter barbells fitted.

The length of a barbell plays an important role in keeping the tongue piercing healthy. For example, too short a piece of jewellery can form small oval dents in the top surface of the tongue. On the other hand, too long a barbell can split the tongue and cause tooth and other complications. BCRs worn near the tip of the tongue run the increased risk of tooth and gum damage.

Healing Time

Minimum two months.

Extra Care Considerations

Swelling is the primary concern with tongue piercings. Regular sucking of ice cubes can help keep this under control. Tightening of the threaded balls is essential to ensure that they don't become detached and inhaled.

Tongue Tied

This is the term used to describe the condition in people who have no space between the underside of their tongue and the floor of the mouth. In many cases piercing the tongue before having had corrective surgery is not possible.

Other kinds of tongue piercing ...

Lingula Fraenum or Tongue Web

A horizontal piercing through the lower tongue fraenum, located on the underside of the tongue, in the flesh that joins the tongue with the floor of the mouth.

Lower Lip

Description and Location

Although the piercing can be placed anywhere along the lower lip, it is usually located below the lip line and vertically central to the face.

Healing Time

Minimum four months.

Types of Suitable Jewellery

Labret studs are normally worn, but BCRs are proving increasingly popular. Only jewellery of a minimum 1.6mm gauge should be worn. Please note that if a BCR is to be worn at a later time, the piercing operative should be informed so that the position can be planned with this in mind.

Extra Care Considerations

Jewellery which is fitted too tightly can pull into the soft lining inside the mouth.

Madonna

Description and Location

Named after the beauty mark worn by the pop phenomenon, Madonna, it is sometimes called the Greta Garbo and Chrome (Cindy) Crawford after their beauty marks. The piercing, like the beauty spot, is located vertically off centre to one side. It is important to remember, as with all piercings, that if the jewellery is removed you will have a permanent scar. Even if only a small one, it is likely to be more noticeable on the face than on other parts of the body.

Types of Suitable Jewellery

If it's a traditional Madonna, a 1.6mm gauge labret stud will be worn, usually one with a jewelled ball fitted at the end.

Healing Times
Minimum of four months.

Twin Madonna
(Symmetrical Upper Lip Piercing)
A Madonna worn as a pair, often positioned high up the lip so that the labret studs are located just below and to either side of the nose.

Filtrum or Medusa
(An Upper Lip Labret)
A labret stud is located central to the face and between the lip line and the nose. Piercing procedure and aftercare is as with the Madonna.

Superior Fraenum
(Smiley or Scrumper)
Pierced in the web of the gum located centrally inside the mouth, behind the upper lip and in front of the teeth and gums. The jewellery used is usually a short barbell or a small internal diameter BCR.

Inferior Fraenum
(Frowny)
Like the superior fraenum, the piercing is located through the gum web located between the lip and the teeth, but this time it is in the lower lip rather than the upper. The jewellery choices and piercing considerations are as with the 'superior fraenum'.

Neck piercings

Front of the neck ...

Pendant (Madison)

Description and Location

Located in the loose fold of skin just above the collarbone. Usually a 1.6mm gauge, curved barbell with plain or jewelled balls, or a BCR is worn. The fashion of wearing pendants hung from clear nylon cords has made this piercing more popular and, in this case, the chain is truly invisible.

Back of the neck ...

Oblongata (Nape)

Description and Location

Located at the back of the neck in the loose flesh between the shoulders and the head. Usually worn as a horizontal piercing with barbells fitted. The length of the barbell varies in length from 12–40mm. Because of the large amount of movement associated with the area, the flexible movement allowed by PTFE barbells is preferred. Metal balls can be worn on the ends of the PTFE barbell. This piercing can take some time to heal – often six months, sometimes longer than a year.

Ear piercings

History: Evidence of ear piercing exists in virtually all ancient and modern societies. In present Western societies over 80 per cent of the female population have their ears pierced. The British Museum has an exhibit of the remains from a Sumerian grave dated 2600BC, showing evidence of pierced ears, and it is believed that the great Roman emperor, Julius Caesar (59BC), wore a ring, probably made of gold, in his ear lobe. In Western Europe the wearing of earrings has maintained its popularity throughout the ages. They were worn by Sir Walter Raleigh, explorer and favourite of Queen Elizabeth I of England; Sir Francis Drake wore one when, in 1588, he routed the Spanish Armada. The great scribe himself, William Shakespeare, also wore one.

Description and Location

Most of the ear, with the exception of the lower lobe, is made up of cartilage. Cartilage is an elastic fibre that constructs and forms the basic shape of the ear. The blood supply to the parts of the ear made of cartilage is poorer than to the fleshy lobe. Most parts of the ear are pierced and the choices are many and varied.

Methods of Ear Piercing

Because of the popularity of ear piercing, including the cartilage parts of the upper ear, there is pressure to use a simple system that can be used by many people with minimal basic training. The piercing of the ear lobe is mostly carried out safely by use of a specialist ear piercing system, commonly called a piercing 'gun'.

Spring Trigger Ear-piercing Systems – 'Guns'

These are intended for use only on the soft flesh of the lobe and the flat upper ear cartilage. There is strong scientific evidence to show that when a stud 7mm long and between 1.2–1.6mm gauge is used, reduced incidences of complications occur. In upper ears, the use of a gun should be restricted to only the flat areas of the ear cartilage. Body piercers in the main don't like the use of gun systems, preferring to use a needle.

Procedure

If the hair is styled in a way that covers the piercing it should be tied back out of the way. Expect to be seated when you are pierced. The area to be pierced is then cleaned and the position marked. If a needle is used, forceps will be applied with little discomfort. The area tends to bleed after the jewellery has been fitted, sometimes for a few minutes. The same procedure can be carried out on areas of flat ear cartilage with a specialist ear piercing system.

Swelling

Swelling should only last a few days. However, pressure from sleeping on the piercing and snagging on clothing can aggravate it, causing swelling which might last for several weeks.

Types of suitable jewellery ...

Ear lobes

Traditional jewellery manufacturers make vast ranges of ear lobe jewellery. New jewellery is often fitted too soon and unhygienic-ally. With ear lobes it is generally better to change the jewellery only after two months.

Upper Ear Cartilage

To encourage speedy healing and reduce the incidence of compli-cations, any jewellery should be 1.6mm gauge until the piercing has healed. The length of the jewellery post is a critical factor in reducing the incidence of abscess and infection complications, 7mm being the optimum length. Changing to conventional 'thin' post ear jewellery can lead to serious complications, particularly if done before the piercing has fully healed, which takes a minimum of four months.

Stretching

Stretching is a common practice with ear lobe piercings where the small hole is gradually enlarged. This should not be attempted in the cartilage of upper ears which does not stretch like the soft fatty tissue of the lobe.

Inner Ear

In body piercing, this refers to the area of the ear (auricle) located outside of the head, but within the outer rim of the ear. This should not be confused with the medical term 'inner ear', which refers to the ear located internally and accessed via the ear canal.

Different styles of ear piercing ...

Lobe

Description and Location

The lobe is the soft fleshy part of the lower ear and consists of skin-covered connective fatty tissue.

Procedure

Most commonly carried out with a specialist spring trigger ear lobe piercing gun. Bleeding is unlikely.

Swelling

If the ear swells excessively, the jewellery can be replaced with a longer labret stud or a BCR.

Types of Suitable Jewellery

Fitting traditional ear jewellery too early can lead to infections and the formation of misshaped piercing holes. If you faithfully follow the aftercare instructions, in later years you will have a small smooth round hole in the lobe of each ear – never a slit.

Multiple Piercings

It is common, particularly amongst women, to have several piercings in each ear lobe. The distance between piercings should be carefully considered so that one piece of jewellery doesn't migrate into the hole of another, and to prevent the back clasps from overlapping.

Upper ear cartilage piercings . . .

Pinna (Helix)

Description and Location

This is probably, along with the auricle, the most common piercing after the lobe. The pinna is located along the uppermost flat outer face of the ear. Care should be taken that the location of the jewellery is not too close to the outer edge of the ear, otherwise migration and rejection can occur. Provided that the ear cartilage is flat, it can be pierced safely using a specialist ear cartilage gun.

Types of Suitable Jewellery

BCRs and labret studs are most commonly worn, although barbells are another option.

Auricle

Description and Location

The flat part of the ear cartilage located in the middle of the ear between the lobe and the pinna. Along with the pinna, this is probably the most popular ear piercing after the ear lobe. Care should be taken not to place the piercing too close to the outer edge of the ear, where it might migrate or be pulled out if snagged on clothing. Only the flat part of the ear can be pierced safely using a specialist ear cartilage gun.

Rook

Description and Location

An inner ear cartilage piercing, located in the upper auricle fold approximately 12–25mm from the top of the ear. To protect the piercing from migrating, or being accidentally pulled out, it is important that sufficient cartilage is available. A general guideline is that, if you can take hold of this area of the ear between the finger and thumb, there is a possibility that a piercing can be safely located. This piercing should only be done with a needle.

Types of Suitable Jewellery

The jewellery used can be a barbell or a BCR. The most effective is a BCR. A lot of people want to have a tiny piece of jewellery fitted initially, particularly in the ears. Fitting a minimum of 1.6mm gauge jewellery reduces the possibility of complications.

Conch

Description and Location

Placed in the shell of the inner ear, a little above the lobe. When selecting a location for this piercing it is important to consider where and how the jewellery will sit at the back of the ear. If it is placed inappropriately it can cause discomfort, particularly during sleep. Only a needle should be used for this piercing.

Types of Suitable Jewellery

A labret stud, with its flat plate located at the back of the ear, is often the most comfortable piece to wear, although a barbell or a larger BCR can also be worn.

Diath (Crux of Helix)
Description and Location
An inner ear piercing located in the crux of the helix, which is in the skin-covered cartilage fold just above the opening to the ear canal, and directly below the rook piercing. It is important that your piercer is happy that a sufficient amount of cartilage is available to protect the piercing from migrating, or being accidentally pulled out through the skin. This is a needle-only piercing.

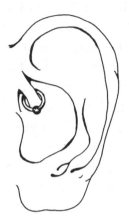

Types of Suitable Jewellery
Barbells can be worn, although a BCR is often most effective.

Forward Pinna
(Forward Helix)
Description and Location
It is located at the front rim of the ear just above the tragus. It looks its best if the finished piece of jewellery is designed to fall into the space just above the tragus.

Types of Suitable Jewellery
Either barbells, BCRs or labret studs can be worn.

Tragus
Description and Location
The firm flap of skin-covered cartilage located at the front entrance to the ear canal, above the point where the upper and

lower jaw bones meet. Only a needle should be used to perform this piercing.

Extra Care Considerations

Swelling can be severe and, in some cases, can last for several weeks. To avoid minor infections the earwax should be regularly cleaned away from the entrance of the ear canal. Locating the jewellery too close to the face can lead to discomfort.

Types of Suitable Jewellery

Severe initial swelling is common, and the jewellery should be long enough to cope. BCRs and labret studs are most popular.

Vertical Tragus

A variation on the Tragus

The vertical tragus is, as the name suggests, a vertical piercing of the tragus.

Anti-Tragus

Description and Location

A needle-only piercing located on the outer rim of the ear, opposite the tragus and just above the lobe. In some cases it is too small to be pierced.

Types of Suitable Jewellery

Barbells and BCRs are most popular in this location.

Scaffold or Industrial

Description and Location

Two separate ear rim piercings are designed to fit a single long barbell. Initially they are treated as two separate piercings and, when healed, the longer scaffold barbell is then fitted. This area can be multiple pierced to great effect, with two or more bars fitted parallel with each other. They can also be designed to sit diagonally forming a cross, as well as being placed vertically from the pinna at the top

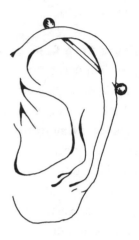

to the lobe at the bottom. This is a variation on weaving and should only be carried out using a needle.

Procedure

A technical piercing where the alignment of the two piercings is crucial, requiring careful planning and preparation. Miscalculation can result in a finished piercing that distorts the natural shape of the ear.

Swelling

This piercing creates four, rather than two, piercing holes. If one piece of jewellery were fitted through all four holes, the swelling might be too great and, for this reason, it is treated as two piercings.

Types of Suitable Jewellery

Whilst the two piercings are being treated separately, BCRs or short barbells are fitted. When the piercing has healed, at least four months later, a full length barbell can be fitted. Typically the barbell ranges between 26–40mm in length with a minimum gauge of 1.6mm.

Orbital

Similar to the scaffold but, in this case, the piercing holes are much closer together so that a BCR can be worn through the piercing. This is usually done on the flat part of the upper ear and rim.

Weave or Stitch Piercing

Where one piece of jewellery is interwoven with two or more piercings. This kind of elaborate piercing needs considerable forward planning with a piercing operative. This is commonly carried out on ears when it is sometimes called an 'ear project', or an 'industrial'. It can also be applied to other parts of the body, particularly on flat skin.

Snug

The piercing travels through the ridge of cartilage that forms the inner shell of the ear, not the outer ear rim. Barbells are best worn initially, but BCRs can be worn when healed.

Torso piercings

Midriff . . .

History: Evidence of navel piercings was found in the mummified remains of the Egyptian Pharaoh Akhenaton, who died in 1400BC. The piercing of the navel in Egyptian and Inca cultures was regarded as having spiritual significance, and was reserved for only the elite members of their societies. Aztec princesses had their navels pierced as a sign of royal status. For Egyptian royalty it was seen as one of the essential requirements for their most important rite of passage, believing that it protected the wearer during the journey between this life and the next.

Navel (upper Belly Button)

Description and Location

This is commonly referred to as the 'belly button' piercing. Located in the upper fold of skin above the navel, this piercing has caught the imagination of many Western females, and is just catching on amongst men. Natural navel designs fall into two main categories: 'outies' and 'innies'. 'Innies' are the most common and are so named because the navel forms an inward shaped hole, and is ideally suited to piercing. On the other hand, 'outies' are navels which project outwards. They are less common and can't always be pierced. 'Outies' occur most commonly in teenage girls. Later in life most 'outies' start to develop into 'innies'.

Procedure

Expect to partially undress. The navel will be cleaned and marked while you are in the standing position, and then you will need to lie flat on your back for the remainder of the procedure. Forceps are gently applied to hold a small fold of skin in position for an accurate piercing to be carried out safely. A small amount of bleeding some-times occurs for a few minutes. Once the piercing has been checked, an adhesive dressing is applied.

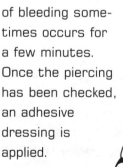
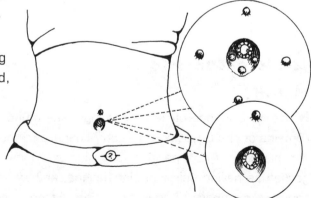

Healing Time

At least five months. Sometimes as long as a year.

Swelling

The flesh around the piercing will swell, but this is not usually noticeable and within a week or two it returns back to normal.

Types of Suitable Jewellery

Any jewellery should be a minimum of 1.6mm gauge, the most popular style being the jewelled navel bar. BCRs are also worn. The initial jewellery will have been selected to allow for swelling. Within 2–6 weeks the jewellery may appear slack, with the barbell projecting outward from the top piercing hole. This is a good indication that you should return to your piercing operative to consider fitting a new down-sized piece of jewellery.

Extra Care Considerations

The navel is the scar resulting from the severing of the umbilical chord after birth. It has a poorer blood supply than normal skin and this can lead to prolonged healing times. Avoid tight fitting clothing around the waistline.

Navel (lower Belly Button)

A piercing, as the name suggests, of the lower section of the navel. It is effectively a mirror image of the upper navel piercing. Although the procedure is very much the same as with upper navels, there are some significant differences. Muscle tone is tighter in the lower navel than the upper and more people complain of discomfort and tightening pains with this piercing. Having a piercing operative that understands how this part of the anatomy moves is crucial to having a comfortable piercing.

Types of suitable jewellery

The piercing length in a lower navel piercing tends to be shorter than in an upper navel piercing. If the navel already has an upper jewelled navel bar fitted, it is best to fit a curved barbell with smaller balls or a BCR.

Navel (Side)

This is the least common of all navel piercings, and is usually worn as an adornment to either a top, or top and bottom navel piercing. Small curved barbells can be worn in pairs and are often designed as part of a four-way piercing, creating the appearance of a cross. When done well this piercing can be very effective. In order to achieve this stunning effect, it is vital that the lines all run true horizontally and vertically. Sometimes all four piercings are performed in one session, although it is preferable for them to be broken down into two or more sessions, which can reduce the possibility of complications (see illustration on page 68).

Navel Scaffold (Industrial)

A top and bottom navel piercing joined by one piece of jewellery. It can also be worn 'side to side'.

Chest ...

History: It is believed that as early as 753BC, newly promoted Roman centurions, during an initiation ritual, had a nipple pierced, their superior courage being further paraded before their troops by hanging their military capes from the piercing.

Following the Crusades, the practice of wearing gold nipple rings as a sign of status spread to Western Europe. For women in the court of the 14th Century Bavarian Queen Isabella, the wearing of garments with extremely low cut necklines became fashionable. Indeed, some outfits were cut to the navel, revealing much of their breasts, which were adorned with nipple rings interconnected with fine gold chains. These were then decorated with equally intricately designed shields and plates. The fashion for wearing nipple jewellery peaked again in late nineteenth century England, with the wearing of a bosom ring being popular amongst the upper classes.

Procedure

Both men and women will usually be asked to undress to the waist. It is important to be seated for this piercing so that the chest or breast is hanging normally. The area will be cleaned and forceps gently applied to hold the nipple still during piercing. Expect some bleeding for a few minutes. A dressing should be applied after the piercing has been checked in a mirror.

WOMEN – Nipples being erectile, have a tendency to change dramatically in shape. To ensure that the piercing is at the very base of the nipple, it is important that the nipple be erect during the marking of the skin. The piercing will be marked at the base of the nipple as close to the breast as possible, at the point where the nipple joins the areola.

MEN – Where necessary an area, of approximately 50mm around the areola, should be cleared of body hair. The piercing will be marked at a distance on the areola at either side of the nipple.

Swelling

Swelling occurs quickly, but is not usually too severe, reducing to normal after two weeks. Increased sensation occurs, which can cause tenderness and, in some cases, a re-occurring mild swelling.

Healing Time

Full healing can be as early as four months, but usually it needs at least six. Nipples can appear to have healed and then suddenly a small secretion appears as a crust on the jewellery. This is usually as a result of a monthly change in hormone levels and in the case of women the rising of a fluid to maintain the opening of the milk ducts.

Types of suitable jewellery

The skin of the nipple is easily torn if snagged, and therefore a minimum of 1.6mm gauge jewellery is recommended. Both BCRs and barbells are commonly worn. Jewellery can be customised using the large array of add-ons and shields which are available.

Female Nipple

Description and Location

The nipple is commonly pierced for both visual and sexual pleasure. Most popularly pierced horizontally from side to side, more unusual is the vertical top to bottom or diagonal piercing. Legal minimum age requirements generally apply for this piercing and, in Britain, a female is required to be over 16 years of age.

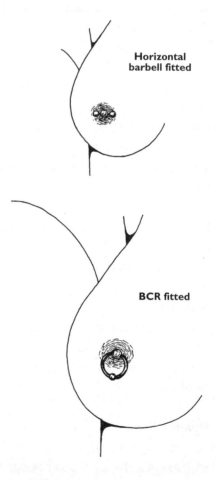

Horizontal
barbell fitted

BCR fitted

Extra Care Considerations

During the first few weeks after the piercing, improved comfort can be found by wearing breast pads designed for nursing mothers. Female breasts and nipples may change in size and shape during the monthly cycle. This should be noted and considered when selecting any new jewellery. If small lumps occur behind the nipple, these should be investigated by a medical practitioner.

Breast Feeding

Available research upon the impact of nipple piercing on breast feeding is poor. Women who have been pierced have reported few or no difficulties. Usually, when the nipple is pierced, only a few milk ducts are severed; many more remain intact, allowing a regular flow of milk from the breast. Some mothers keep their jewellery in place whilst others remove it when feeding their babies. A note of caution: any balls or beads could become loosened and there is a danger of the infant inhaling or swallowing the jewellery.

Body Modification

Some people have their nipples pierced in an attempt to reverse inverted nipples. Indeed, Victorian doctors used to prescribe nipple piercing as a potential cure for both inverted and small nipples in order that they would be better able to breast feed. Some women like to train their nipples to become longer. By fitting rings or collars around the nipple and gradually changing them with collars of a greater thickness, the nipple will become stretched in length.

Brooch Piercing

This is worn, mainly by women, off centre and in the upper part of the breast. It is often customised with great effect by wearing a shield or add-on made of silver or gold, or UV plastic for clubbing. The appearance is very much like that of a brooch, but, instead of being worn on the clothing, it is worn on the skin.

Cleavage Piercing

A piercing placed in the centre of the breasts, again this is generally worn by women. A vertical curved barbell, when wearing a low-cut top, gives an appearance similar to that of the pendant piercing.

Male Nipple

Description and Location

Commonly pierced for both visual and sexual pleasure. The nipple protrusion of the male chest is located approximately in the centre of the pectoral muscle. Most commonly pierced singularly, but sometimes in pairs, and positioned horizontally across the areola. The vertical top to bottom piercing is, like in women, less common, as are double piercings, where both vertical and horizontal piercings are worn in one nipple. To reduce the possibility of accidental removal of the jewellery from snagging, the male nipple is pierced either side of the nipple so that the jewellery passes through the back, rather than through the actual nipple.

Extra Care Considerations

Care should be taken not to snag jewellery on clothing and objects, particularly when lifting, playing sport or engaging in horse play. Sometimes, when hormonal changes occur in the body, a secretion will be discharged through the nipple, and may form on the jewellery as a crust. If a lump appears behind the nipple, a medical opinion should be sought.

Horizontal barbell

Horizontal BCR

Vertical barbell

Diagonal barbell

Intimate piercings below the waist

Female intimate piercings ...

The area of the female sex organs is referred to as the vulva. Women are attracted to having their vulva pierced for many reasons not least that it is seen as being sexy. The allure for some is the possibility of a heightened sexual sensation, whilst, for others, it is the thought of being kinky. Women on the whole have found that wearing rings, bracelets, necklaces and other jewellery helps them both look and feel more feminine and attractive. Wearing jewellery in their innermost sanctum of feminine sensuality might be seen as a natural extension of these kinds of metal adornment.

The legality of having a piercing for the purpose of sexual gratification in English law is unclear. Given this climate of legal uncertainty, most piercing operatives will be prepared to pierce genitalia, but may, for reasons of sensible caution, be reluctant to engage in conversation about the possible sexual benefits of piercings.

History: Ensuring chastity was probably the motivation behind early intimate female piercing. Men in early civilisations considered women to be their possessions. The value of a woman's virginity before marriage, and faithfulness after, could be guaranteed by piercing the female sex organs. This was usually achieved by piercing the outer labia with rings and then connecting them with some sort of lock. Romans used these methods to prevent female slaves from engaging in sexual intercourse with their male counterparts.

Piercing Procedures

Choosing a piercing operative that you can trust and feel comfortable with is a very important consideration. With all intimate piercings you will need to undress below the waist. For this reason, it is best to wear clothing that is easily removed. Thoroughly wash the area to be pierced directly before your appointment. To ensure an accurate piercing, measuring and marking the piercing is very important. Female genital piercing can be the most difficult piercing to align and mark. Once pierced, a small amount of bleeding occurs, stopping usually within a few minutes. A panty liner worn immediately after the piercing and for the next few days can help improve personal comfort. There can be major differences in the design of female genitalia. Therefore the viability of a particular piercing is dependent upon these individual anatomical variations, and, in some cases, a piercing is either inappropriate or not possible.

Swelling
The traumatised skin in the immediate piercing area will swell, but this is not usually excessive and generally recedes within a few days.

Healing Time
Most genital piercings are normally trouble-free and quickly heal. The healing period can be as little as three months, although, in some cases, this can extend to over six months.

Types of Suitable Jewellery
Although most female vulva piercings are carried out using 1.6mm gauge jewellery, in order to avoid any 'cheesewire' or migration complications, it is advisable, once the piercing is healed, to 'up-size' to 2.0mm or 2.4mm jewellery. Both BCRs and barbells are worn, the suitability of each varying according to the piercing types and position. Specially designed labret studs can also be worn in the labia.

Extra Care Considerations
Don't have a piercing whilst you are menstruating. The flesh of the vulva is easily irritated. Pressure from bodily movement and rub from clothing can lead to the development of minor sores and

abrasions. Inner horizontal vulva piercing can be prone to migrate or park in a new position. This can be alleviated by checking daily and applying saltwater to clean the area. With pressure of movement, jewellery of too small a gauge can lead to enlargement of the piercing holes, and may cause tearing.

Clitoris

Description and Location

This piercing is situated above the vaginal opening, just above the urinary tract, and is often covered by the skin of the clitoris hood. When this skin is withdrawn, the clitoris appears as a smooth pea-shaped organ, which runs upwards into the skin of the pubis. There are enormous variations in the size of the clitoris head. In order for it to be pierced safely, it needs to be of sufficient size to accommodate 1.6mm gauge jewellery comfortably. Piercing too

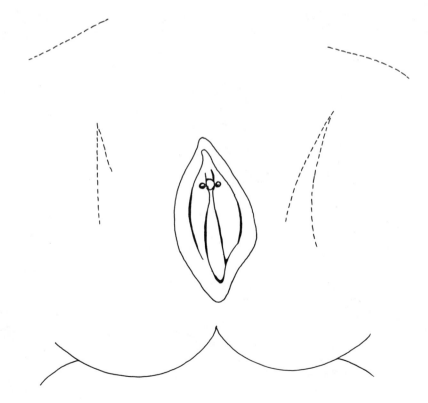

small a clitoris risks causing nerve damage, and loss of sensation. Normally the clitoris is pierced horizontally from side to side, and a BCR or a small barbell is fitted.

Clitoris Hood
Description and Location

This clitoris head is a thin layer of folded skin situated around the clitoris, often totally covering it. The exact location of the piercing and the choice of jewellery vary between individuals. Normally, when pierced horizontally, a BCR is worn. A barbell (often curved) is the popular choice when the hood is pierced vertically.

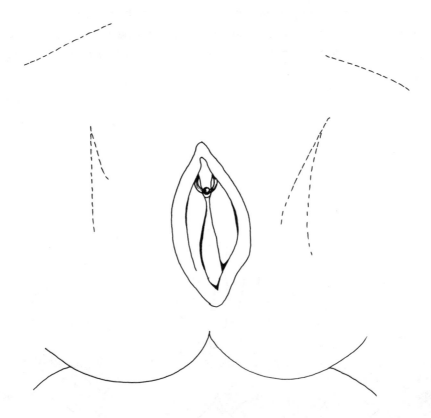

Triangle

A piercing located between the clitoris shaft and the urethra. Usually worn with a BCR. It is reputed to be the most sexually gratifying of all female piercings.

Outer Labia

Description and Location

The labia are the outer pair of lips that protect the female genitalia. They are hair-covered, fleshy folds of skin, containing sweat glands. It is best to shave any hair from the labia before they are pierced. Usually BCRs are worn, although specially designed labret studs are available.

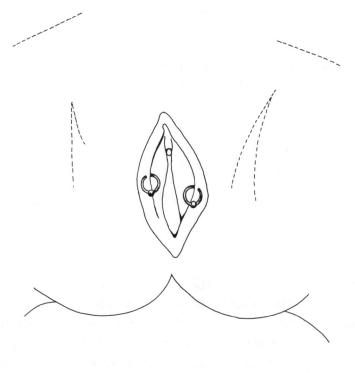

Inner Labia

Description and Location

The hairless inner folds of the labia are covered by the larger outer labia. The exact shape and location may vary between individuals. The jewellery choices are much the same as for the outer labia.

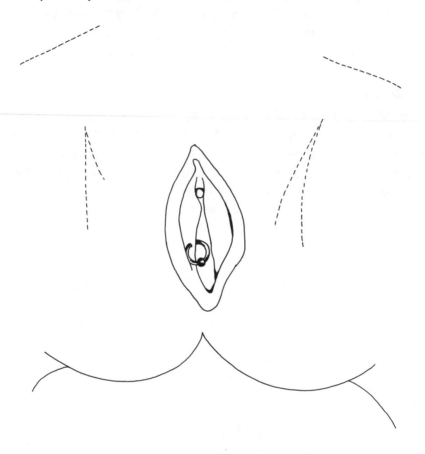

Male intimate piercings ...

Many men are concerned that having an intimate piercing will be extremely painful. Indeed, for most men the very thought makes their toes curl. After having a penis piercing, most men's reaction is that they experienced a sharp, but short pain, lasting usually only a second or two, and generally it was nowhere near as painful as they feared.

When talking about a penis piercing, most people are refer-ring to the Prince Albert which is abbreviated to 'PA'. Few men, when considering having a penis piercing, are aware of the large number of different types of piercings available, and know even less about their significance.

People have intimate piercings for all sorts of reasons. Sex is one of the major ones. The allure of being seen to be kinky is an attractive proposition to some people. Others find it can heighten their own and their partner's sexual experience.

History: The piercing of the male penis dates back to ancient times. The vertical piercing of the penis glans with a metal barbell, called the apadravya, is a piercing that has been used in Asia for thousands of years, and is mentioned in the Kama Sutra.

Foreskin piercing is a tradition dating back to Greek and Roman times. To prevent their slaves from having sex, Romans pierced their male slaves, linking the foreskin and the scrotum.

During the 1820s it became very fashionable for English gentlemen to wear tight-fitting Beau Brummel trousers. To avoid the neat lines being broken with the bulge of genitalia, tailors designed trousers with fasteners, so that the penis, when pierced with a ring called a 'dress ring', could be attached. Today the tradition amongst tailors continues: when fitting a pair of trousers, they ask if the gentleman dresses to the right or left.

Piercing Procedure

The penis needs to be flaccid when pierced. This is not usually a problem. For most men, the clinical process of revealing their genitalia is enough to cause their penis to shrink in size. Any piercing operative will know and expect this. The whole of the genitalia should be washed thoroughly before the piercing appoint-ment. Measuring and marking the position before carrying out the piercing is a very important part of the procedure, helping to ensure an accurate piercing.

Swelling

Any swelling will usually last for only a few days. Intermittent swelling can be experienced with some piercings, which can be aggravated by excessive movement, such as when carrying out physical and manual labour, sports and exercising.

Healing Times

This varies from three months to over a year. Piercings that pass through the urethra split into two separate shorter piercings and tend to heal a little more quickly than other piercings. The flow of healthy urine helps to flush out any harmful bacteria.

Types of Suitable Jewellery

To avoid skin tears, it is advisable that any initial piercing jewellery be at least 2.4mm gauge, and it is further advisable, when the piercing has healed, to up-size the jewellery to larger 3.2mm gauge. The friction experienced during sexual intercourse can put extreme stress on a penis piercing. Jewellery of thinner gauge may cut through the skin like a wire through cheese.

It is not uncommon for penis piercings to be gradually 'up-sized' with jewellery of gauges between 4mm and 10mm. Some men go as far as stretching up to 20mm jewellery. The choice of jewellery is often determined by the type of piercing, and both BCRs and barbells can be worn. For example, PA piercings are more suited to BCRs, whilst apadravya and palang piercings are designed for wearing a barbell. Other piercings, like the scrotum, can be left to personal choice.

Extra Care Considerations

Most genital piercings bleed, usually stopping after a few minutes. Sometimes the bleeding recurs in very small amounts over the following week. The wearing of a panty liner for the first few days can help prevent both blood marked clothing and discomfort. Regular saltwater baths and soaks will help with healing.

It is best to refrain from sexual intercourse for 3–6 weeks after a piercing, and then it should be carried out only gently with extreme caution. A piercing, until healed, is an open wound. The use of a condom during sex to protect against disease transmission is urged. With genital piercings, a good airflow is essential for smooth healing. This is particularly relevant with scrotum piercings. The pressure of the foreskin on piercings in the penis head can cause jewellery to migrate, or park in a new position. This can be avoided by keeping the foreskin retracted during the first few weeks.

Foreskin (Kuno)

In ancient Greece athletes performed in the nude. To keep their genitalia out of the way whilst performing in sporting events, and to prevent them misusing much needed energy engaging in sex beforehand, their foreskins were pierced and linked to a scrotum piercing.

Description and Location

Carried out as one or as a pair of piercings. The foreskin is a retractable fold of skin that covers the head of the penis. It is pierced through the end, towards its opening. Expect some swelling, which, if aggravated by movement between the penis head and clothing, can worsen after a few days. To avoid a tear, care should be taken when withdrawing the foreskin.

Fraenulum
Description and Location

The fraenulum is a flange of skin located on the underside of the penis which connects the foreskin and the glans that form the penis head. The fraenulum doesn't always remain after circumcision. Small BCRs or very short barbells are worn. For occasional wear, a large internal diameter BCR can be worn. This is also reputed, when positioned tightly around the penis, to help maintain an erection.

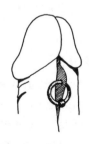

Scrotum

Description and Location

The scrotum is the pouch of skin that hangs behind the penis and contains the testicles. Piercings can be placed on most parts of the scrotum, which lends itself to being multiple-pierced. Scrotum piercings are popular and usually successful, provided sensible precautions are followed. Tight clothing restricts ventilation. Rub-

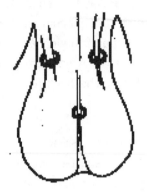

bing caused during heavy manual work, or through sporting activities can lead to complications such as secondary swelling. In such cases healing can be extended to over a year. Generally, BCRs are worn, as well as barbells which are often curved.

Hafada

A piercing of the scrotum, the hafada originates in the Middle East, where adolescent boys are pierced on the lefthand side of the scrotum with rings. In the West, the hafada is pierced at either side of the scrotum crease, in the folds of skin above each testicle, and is commonly worn in pairs, one on each side.

Lorum

The lorum scrotum piercing is placed horizontally across the vertical seam of the scrotum. BCRs and short barbells are usually worn.

Pubic

Located in a soft fold of skin just above the penis, this piercing, because of anatomical differences between the male and female pubis, is generally considered to be a piercing for a man. A similar piercing can be done for women, located at the top of the clitoris, called a Christina.

Guiche

Description and Location

This piercing is positioned horizont-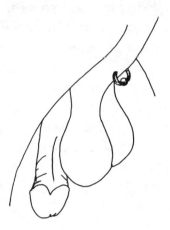
ally across the line of the perineum,
and located between the scrotum
and the anus. The area of the
perineum is loaded with nerve cells,
making it highly sensitive to touch,
and this piercing is reputed to
heighten pleasure during sex. This is
not an easy location to see and
agrée its position, so, unless you are
a contortionist, you will have to rely
on drawings and trust in your piercing operative. Expect some
swelling. If it is aggravated by movement, particularly in warm
sticky weather, it can worsen after a few days. Prolonged seating,
such as driving a motor vehicle, can lead to secondary swelling, as
can vigorous exercise. Scrupulous toilet hygiene procedures will
need to be followed. 2.4mm BCRs are the most popular choice of
jewellery, although straight and curved barbells can be worn.

Palang

In various Pacific Islands of South East Asia, this piercing is worn
to give enhanced pleasure during sexual intercourse. Men from
the Dayak, Iban and Kelabit tribes of Borneo have their penis
pierced in adulthood. A feather is worn in the piercing. This is
removed and replaced with a metal bar, called an ampallang, before
engaging in sex. The Dayak name 'ampallang' translates to 'crossbar'. The women in these tribes believe that having sex with a
man not wearing an ampallang is inferior to intercourse with a
crossbar in place. In the West, the distinction between the name
for the piece of jewellery, and the name of the piercing, 'palang',
is not always made, so sometimes this piercing is referred to as
an ampallang.

Description and Location

A horizontal (side to side) piercing of the male penis glans. It can either travel through the urethra, or above or below it. A piercing through the urethra tends to heal more quickly than one longer piercing. A barbell is meant to be worn in a palang, although a ring can be worn. The gauge should be at least 2.4mm. Foreskin

pressure on the piercing may cause the jewellery to migration or park in a new position. Either way it can take some time to heal – at least six months.

Prince Albert

Today in the West, the piercing of the penis head is often referred to as the Prince Albert, or abbreviated to 'PA'. This is after the German Prince Albert of Saxe-Coburg-Gotha, who became the husband of Queen Victoria. He is believed to have had the piercing prior to his marriage to the English Queen in 1840.

Description and Location

When a person talks about a penis pierc-ing, the PA is usually what they mean. The piercing travels through the urethra opening in the head of the penis, and exits underneath to one side of the fraenulum. The piercing passes through the urethra and normally heals more quickly than most piercings. Sometimes very quick healing

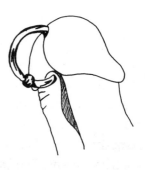

may be apparent at the outer piercing holes, whilst the deeper inner fistula will take at least three months before fully forming. A 2.4mm gauge BCR is normally fitted in the initial piercing.

Extra Care Considerations

Occasional light bleeding may occur for the first few days after piercing.

Reverse Prince Albert

Description and Location

As the name indicates, this piercing is located in the reverse position of the Prince Albert. Again, it travels through the penis entrance, along the urethra and, instead of travelling down, it travels upwards and exits through the top of the penis glans. The procedure, healing requirements, jewellery sizes and aftercare are the same as for the PA.

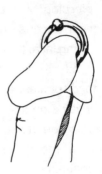

Apadravya

Around 600–700AD, this piercing was included in a book, called the Karma Sutra, which describes and illustrates a large number of sexual acts. In South Eastern Asia, sex without such a piercing is seen as inferior.

Description and Location

A vertical piercing of the penis. Located centrally, it travels from the fraenulum up through the urethra. Usually through the head but some-times through the length of the penis, behind the glans. Healing tends to be quicker when the urethra has been pierced. It is usual to have a 2.4mm gauge barbell fitted, although a ring can be worn. In uncircumcised men, the pressure of the foreskin may result in migration or jewellery parking in another position.

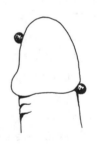

Dydoe

It is believed that this piercing was developed by circumcised men, who wished to recreate the sensation of their missing fore-skin for their sexual partners.

Description and Location

A piercing of the penis glans through the dorsal corona, usually done in pairs. The piercing starts from the top of the penis, at the rear of the glans, and travels a short distance before surfacing about halfway along the penis head. A penis head with large dorsal shaped coronas on the  top is most suited to this piercing. If the coronas are less pronounced, it can be too shallow, leading to jewellery rejection. Normally, a pair of 2.4mm gauge curved barbells is fitted.

Other piercings . . .

Hand Web

This is usually pierced in the web of skin between the thumb and forefinger, although this can be worn in the skin webs between any of the fingers. It is usually initially carried out with a BCR, then, when the swelling has gone down, it can be changed to a barbell, often curved. The area to be pierced will be cleaned, but it is also a good idea to give your hands a good wash before your appointment. Skin around the piercing remains swollen (this gives the area a puffy appearance, usually painless) for up to six weeks. The area needs to return to normal before the jewellery can be changed for a finished size barbell. Hand washing is always an important part of any piercing aftercare procedure, particularly so in this case. Some occupations are not suited to this piercing: for example, where the hands are exposed to dirt and grease, or prolonged dexterity is maintained in holding instruments or typing on keyboards.

Creative (Flat Skin or Skin to Skin)

Flat skin piercings are carried out on parts of the body that don't have an obvious fold of flesh, in which to place and hang jewellery. They can be located on most parts of the body. These piercings have a higher incidence of success when they are placed on skin that has thicker underlying layers of fatty tissue, rather than where the skeletal bone is near to the surface. Muscular areas that are subject to regular flexing and contracting movements are also best avoided. Flat skin piercings are often carried out as part of a larger, more complex piercing pattern or design, and are sometimes done as a temporary piercing for a special occasion.

Because these piercings are carried out on flat areas of skin, the surface tension puts increased pressure on the jewellery, particularly at the point where it punctures the skin. For this reason, conventional jewellery, such as straight and curved barbells or BCRs, has a high incidence of migration and total rejection. A greater success rate can be achieved where specially designed staple jewellery is fitted. Staples are barbells that are made with an angled bend of 22.5 to 45 degrees towards both ends of the post. This lesser angle reduces both jewellery and skin tension, making rejection less likely. Threaded balls are screwed onto the ends of the post just like a normal barbell.

Achilles or Ankle

As the name suggests, this is a piercing of the ankle, in the soft skin folds at the side and at the heel. Because of the regular movement and the extreme skin tension that often occur in this area, these piercings are prone to complications, in particular migration or rejection.

Re-piercing . . .

Where jewellery has been removed or rejected by the body and the piercing has healed over, sometimes a person wants to have another attempt at keeping the piercing – this is then termed a re-piercing. Re-piercing is possible in most cases, but it is best to identify the reasons why the initial piercing failed in the first place. This can help reduce the possibility of it happening again.

Chapter Nine

How to care for a piercing

SPECIAL CARE NEEDS to be taken of a piercing immediately after it has been carried out and during the whole of the healing period. Within the trade, ideas on how to care for a piercing vary. This section aims to provide a guide to post-piercing care based upon generally accepted good practice. A lot of common post-piercing complications can be avoided by following a regular care routine.

Before having a piercing

You should read this section very carefully before choosing a piercing. The information within should help you decide if the piercing you are wanting is the right one for your personal circumstances.

Once you have made your choice and have had the piercing carried out, you will then be responsible for the good care of it for some time to come.

Hand washing

Probably the single most effective action that you can take to care for your piercing is to wash your hands thoroughly before touching it.

Cleaning

There is much debate in the trade and between medical professionals on how best to care for a piercing. The consensus is broken into two main camps: those that advise the application of a cleaning solution and those that don't. This is simplified into 'Bottled' aftercare and 'Routine' aftercare. With both methods, cleaning of the piercing is advocated. Often a combination of both methods proves satisfactory.

Bottled aftercare

Here, the application, at regular intervals throughout the day (2–3 times daily), of a cleaning solution is advised. The most commonly recommended solution is saline (salt water). Saline solution is applied with clean cotton buds or cotton wool to soften, and then remove, any dried crusted material attached to the jewellery and the wound. During the rest of the time, the piercing should be kept dry and well ventilated.

Routine aftercare

Keep the piercing wound as dry as possible. When showering (once or twice daily), use an antibacterial soap to clean away any dried and crusted material from the jewellery and the wound.

Saline solution

Sachets of isotonic saline solution are made especially to match the saline solution in the body (a dilution of 0.9 per cent salt in water), and can be purchased from a pharmacy. Alternatively, you can make your own by dissolving no more than 1/4 teaspoonful of sea salt into 250ml of clean, boiled water and letting it cool.

CAUTION: Never apply hot solution to the skin.

Other kinds of aftercare solutions

There are many kinds of prepared aftercare solutions that are widely available. If you are going to use one of these solutions, it is advisable to carry out a patch test before use. Apply a small amount to a dressing and tape this to the inside crease of the elbow. Check after a few hours for any signs of irritation. If irritation occurs, do not use it. Clean warm tap water may be as useful a solution as any.

Preparations to be avoided

Generally, solutions not recommended for use with a piercing that is still healing, include peroxide and alcohol-based antiseptics. These can be too strong and may cause dryness. Most ointments are not recommended as they can prevent oxygen from reaching the wound, and may possibly lead to complications.

Dressings

The continual wearing of a plaster dressing can help protect the wound from infection by outside bacteria, as well as cushioning the piercing from snagging during rigorous physical activities. The down side to dressings is that any bacteria already at the site of the wound will be incubated and grow much more quickly than if it had been left to ventilate naturally.

A normal new piercing

There is a difference between caring for a conventional wound and a piercing wound. With a conventional wound, the aim is to remove any foreign objects and then quickly re-seal the skin surface. Body piercing aims to trick the body into accepting, rather than rejecting, a piece of metal jewellery. The skin forms a tunnel of flesh called a fistula around the jewellery. This takes time and, whilst the wound remains open, it is at risk from outside infections.

Typically, new piercings are tender, itchy and slightly red, and can remain so for a few weeks. A clear odourless fluid, called plasma, will sometimes discharge from the piercing. Often, when pressure is applied to a piercing from clothing or the jewellery is snagged, a whitish-yellow exudation is secreted from the wound. A crust formed from dried plasma and exudation may attach and tighten around the jewellery as it heals, preventing the jewellery from moving. The exudation should not be confused with a pus-like discharge from an infected piercing.

Bleeding

Most piercings bleed. This stops after a few minutes, and may occasionally re-occur a little during the first few days. If you experience any excessive or continuous bleeding, seek immediate medical assistance. Read the section on blood loss control in chapter 10, 'If things go wrong'.

Swelling

Most piercings will swell to some extent. To allow for this, jewellery inserted into your piercing will be longer than the distance between the piercing holes. Occasionally, however, a piercing may swell more than is normally anticipated, and can become painful, often leading to complications.

Removing jewellery

Many post-piercing complications can be attributed to the early removal of body jewellery. Even though a piercing may appear to have healed on the outside, the inside of the fistula can take several months to form. Replacing jewellery too early can lead to the unhealed fistula becoming damaged, and to an increased possibility of infection.

Sterilising jewellery

To minimise the possibility of wound infection, all jewellery should be properly sterilised, using a medical autoclave, before it is fitted into a piercing. This also applies to any newly purchased jewellery. Applying boiled water or the flame from a lighter is not a proper sterilisation process.

Healing times

The period of initial healing is called the period of epithelisation, and varies between individuals. Each piercing is different and the methods of caring should reflect those differences. The piercing wound will heal first around the outside holes, and then gradually, over several months, the centre of the fistula will form.

Here is a general guide for **minimum** anticipated healing periods. Piercings can sometimes take much longer to heal, occasionally taking over a year.

Ears – lobe	2 months	Lip	3 months
Ears – cartilage	4 months	Tongue	2 months
Nose	4 months	Navel	5 months
Eyebrow	4 months	Nipple	4 months
Cheek	4 months	Genital piercings	3 months

Some common complications and how they can be avoided

Over-cleaning

Vigorous cleaning, using a cleanser that is too strong, or applying it too often, can produce symptoms that are commonly mistaken for an infection. The skin may become very tender, taking on a shiny appearance, and there may be a clear discharge.

Infections

A piercing is a fresh wound. If kept clean and dry, it will heal quickly and completely. However, if it is not kept clean, it can become infected. In severe cases, this can lead to sepsis, urethritis or septicaemia. At the first sign of a possible infection, visit your piercing operative and doctor.

Infections are caused by contact with micro-organisms such as bacteria or fungi, and can often be traced to one of the following activities:

● Touching the piercing with unwashed hands
● Oral contact with the piercing, including your own saliva
● Contact with hair, cosmetics and infrequently washed bedding
● Going into a pool, Jacuzzi, lake, ocean or other body of water

The following are possible indications of an infection:

● Increased redness and swelling
● The piercing is painful to touch
● Painful throbbing or spreading sensation of heat at the piercing site
● Thick discharge with an unusual odour that may be yellow, green or grey in colour

Do not remove jewellery as this may aggravate the problem by closing off drainage for the discharge matter. An infection requires immediate attention. A visit to your local Accident and Emergency Department is appropriate if an infection is suspected.

Warm soaks and compresses

Sometimes, when a piercing is showing signs of irritation or possible mild infection, hot saline soaks and compresses can help. Depending upon the location of the piercing on the body, apply saline solution via cotton wool balls or similar, by pressing onto the area for approximately 10 minutes. Where possible, pour cooled saline solution into an egg cup or small beaker and hold over the area. The suction creates a vacuum seal with the skin, preventing the solution pouring out of the sides.

Metal hypersensitivity

The most commonly identified metal which causes an allergic reaction is nickel. Many metal alloys, such as surgical steel, silver and gold, contain nickel. The appearance of a piercing irritated in this way is sometimes similar to that of an infection. The possibility of a nickel or metal allergy should always be considered in any such complication.

Migration

Sometimes your piercing jewellery can start to move outwards through the skin. This is termed migration. In extreme cases, this can lead to jewellery 'growing out' completely. Some piercings, in particular eyebrows and navels, are more prone to migration than others. Although it is not usually painful, if left unchecked it can lead to the piercing being pulled or torn out of the skin, and can lead to permanent scarring.

Post-piercing check-up

It is a good idea to visit your piercing operative for a check-up after your piercing to be sure everything is healing well. In most cases, this will be between one and four weeks after the piercing.

Piercing – specific aftercare

The following are aftercare issues that are specific to a particular piercing. It is not an exhaustive list, but highlights some of the more common complications that can be avoided.

Ear cartilage piercings

Potentially infectious micro-organisms are easily introduced into the piercing wound. This risk can be avoided by regular hair washing, and styling hair away from the piercing. Regular changing and cleaning of things with which the ear comes into contact, such as bed linen and telephones, is helpful. For the same reason, care should be taken, when using public telephones, not to place the handset next to your new piercing; likewise with head rests on buses and trains. Also never touch the piercing with unwashed fingers. Sleeping posture can put pressure onto the piercing, leading to sores and swellings, as can wearing hats and helmets.

Navel piercings

It is important to maintain a regular flow of oxygen to all piercings and this can be difficult with the navel. Avoiding tightly fitting waistlines and leaving the top button of skirts or trousers un-fastened can be helpful.

Nipple piercings

This piercing can develop a tenderness during the first few weeks of healing. Often it is aggravated by clothing friction and catching against objects. This can be eased and reduced by the wearing of a breast pad inside a bra, for men or, by wearing a breathable dressing.

Genital piercings

Both males and females are advised to use a panty liner to absorb excess moisture and cushion the piercing. Avoid tight restrictive clothing, that can cause irritation or that limits oxygen flow to the area. There may be intermittent bleeding for the first few days after the initial piercing. This bleeding should only be minor; if it is continuous and heavy in flow seek immediate medical attention. Any sexual contact should be gentle and latex barriers used to protect the piercing from your partner's body fluids. With some piercings it is advisable to refrain from full sexual intercourse for at least 2–3 weeks, or until the piercing has completely healed.

Tongue and other oral piercings

Oral piercings require different aftercare routines from other piercings. Generally, piercings in the mouth heal much more quickly than those in other parts of the body. Usually, the most uncomfortable factor with tongue piercings is the swelling, the amount of which varies between individuals. The following guidance can help reduce the effect of the swelling and help prevent any potential complications.

Mouth rinsing

The risk of infection can be reduced by using a hot saltwater mouthwash four times daily. The saline solution should be held in the mouth for at least two minutes. After eating and smoking, the mouth should be rinsed with saltwater or clean water.

Swelling

Swelling can be reduced by sucking ice cubes hourly for the first 24–48 hours after the piercing. Avoid drinking alcohol for 72 hours after piercing as this can aggravate the swelling through dehydration.

Eating

If you have difficulty swallowing food, cut it up into small pieces and, if necessary, use tweezers to place food at the back of the mouth for chewing before swallowing. Drink plenty of non-alcoholic fluids to prevent dehydration. During the first few days after having a tongue piercing, eating spicy foods, such as curries, and acidic fruits, such as oranges and their juices, may cause a painful irritation. Avoid placing foreign objects, such as pens and drinking bottles, into your mouth until the piercing has completely healed.

Calculus formation on metal surfaces

This appears as a white coating, usually on the balls of the barbell. It can be kept under control by including jewellery brushing in any existing oral hygiene routine.

Hyper salivation

With an initial oral piercing it is normal for extra saliva to be created. This should settle back to normal after a few days. If it does not, seek advice, firstly from your piercing operative and then from your dentist.

Scar tissue formation

Oral piercings can develop a build up of scar tissue around the internal piercing hole. This occurs most frequently with tongue piercings, particularly on the underside of the tongue. It forms a white coloured rim or small tube of flesh around the jewellery which normally falls away within 2–3 weeks. If it remains after this time, seek advice from a piercing operative and a dentist.

Obstruction of x-rays

Some dentists may ask you to remove oral jewellery if they need to take x-rays of the mouth. Others might ask you to remove them for all routine procedures. As oral piercings are increasing in popularity, some dentists are taking a more relaxed and understanding approach and don't always demand that jewellery be removed.

Other indirect aftercare considerations

Activities during a normal daily routine can impact upon a new piercing, leading to complications. The following list of some common activities should be considered before being pierced.

Bathing and showering

Bath water is possibly the dirtiest water that your new piercing will encounter. It can be contaminated with bacteria from other parts of your body. It is important that your piercing is not immersed in this water. For example, with a new navel piercing, do not allow the bath water to cover your navel. Do not use a towel to dry a piercing. Instead dab it with a clean paper towel.

Swimming

There is a serious risk of infection from the water of swimming pools, spas, Jacuzzis, saunas, the oceans, lakes and rivers. When entering a body of unknown water the piercing should be treated until healed as any open wound, and ought to be covered with a water resistant dressing.

Clothing

To avoid sores, adjust your clothing so that it doesn't apply pressure or rub against your piercing. Head wear, such as hats, caps, safety and motor bike helmets, is likely to cause irritation. Care should be taken in dressing and undressing when removing clothing over one's head so as not to snag the jewellery.

Posture and body movement

Consider the effect your body movement and posture have upon your new piercing: for example, walking, bending, lifting, washing, grooming your hair, putting on make-up, etc. All these can affect the healing of your piercing. A protective dressing may prevent pressure and rubbing of your piercing, or an adjustment in posture may help.

Cosmetic products

Avoid hair gels, mousse and sprays coming into contact with

the new piercing. Applying cosmetics to the face can also cause irritation with new facial piercings.

Habits

Fiddling and playing with jewellery can lead to the piercing becoming tender or infected.

Hygiene

Working in dirty and dusty atmospheres can make life difficult for any exposed new piercing. Extra care should be taken when working in high risk environments: for example, hospital, doctor's surgery, vet's, etc,

Pastimes

Rigorous movement and increased perspiration from physical exercise, such as working out in the gym or playing sport, can irritate piercings. Padded absorbent dressings can help minimise their impact.

Diet

With all oral piercings, for the first seven days avoid eating spicy foods. Supplements of vitamin C and zinc can help promote healing of the piercing wound.

Visiting dentists, doctors, hospitals

For most medical operating procedures, doctors insist that metal body jewellery be removed so that it doesn't interfere with electronic equipment or get in the way of the procedure. Piercings don't usually interfere with x-rays and can therefore be worn for this procedure. The subject of your body piercings should be brought up as early as possible and you may have to take a firm stand if you want to keep your jewellery in place.

Your piercing operative can replace metal jewellery with PTFE for some procedures. With well healed piercings, if the jewellery is left out for a day or so, it should go back in place without any difficulty. Although, as a note of caution, the fistula in oral piercings will shrink very quickly, making replacement of jewellery difficult after only a few days.

When deciding on a piercing, it is worth considering your next visit to the dentist or any planned medical procedures. Don't have tongue or lip piercings less than six weeks before a dental appointment. If you have surgery planned, consider the implications of that procedure. Give your piercing an ample opportunity to heal, so that if jewellery needs to be removed it is less likely to heal over immediately.

Pregnancy

As above, if you are pregnant, you may be asked to remove your jewellery for scans, etc. In the later stages of your pregnancy the skin of any navel piercings may stretch excessively. Replacing metal jewellery with longer PTFE will help keep your piercing open. Consult your piercing operative, as well as your midwife, early in your pregnancy, so that you have time to become familiar with your options.

Wearing correctly fitting jewellery

With initial piercings, once the swelling has gone down the jewellery can start to feel slack and look sloppy. Skin tears and jewellery migration caused through clothing wear and snagging can be prevented by having the piercing measured regularly and having correctly sized jewellery fitted.

Stretching

This is where the width of the piercing hole is increased. Some people stretch up a piercing after it has healed to personalise it.

The most commonly stretched piercing is the ear lobe, which is often stretched to have a flesh tunnel fitted. Another piercing type that is commonly stretched is the genitalia. This usually applies to males, who wear larger gauge jewellery to help prevent skin tears. Stretching should never be attempted until the piercing has completely healed and then only gradually, by one increment at a time (no more than 0.6mm). No bleeding or tearing should occur.

Re-piercing
Piercings that have healed over can often be re-pierced. Sometimes re-piercings take longer to heal.

Smoking
Tobacco kills the skin tissue, suppresses the immune system, which slows down the healing process, and increases the risk of an infection. This is particularly a problem with any oral piercing.

Sexual activity
Viruses, such as HIV and hepatitis, can enter the body through a piercing wound and can be present in saliva, sweat, semen and vaginal secretions of infected people. Avoid contact with other people's body fluids until the piercing has healed. With oral piercings, this includes kissing and oral sex. In the case of genital piercings, penetrative sex should be refrained from for at least two weeks, and then should be slow and gentle to begin with.

Post-piercing aftercare check-ups
Once the piercing has healed, it is good practice to have it checked by a piercing operative twice a year. This ensures that problems can be prevented and, if they are occurring, for remedial action to be taken.

Cleaning a healed fistula

It takes some time for a piercing fistula to form – in most cases, at least four months after being pierced and longer where complications have occurred. When it does heal, you will have created a new part of your body's anatomy, which requires special care. Every three months, the fistula needs to be flushed clean with saline solution – more often in summer months for piercings that are normally covered by clothing. Remove the jewellery and bathe the fistula with saline solution ensuring that it passes internally between the piercing holes, and then replace the jewellery. This regular maintenance helps cut down the risk of thrush and fungal infections.

Please note

The advice given in this section is based on the author's research, practical experience and consultations with piercing operatives and medical professionals. However, the information is given for guideline purposes only and no legal responsibility can be accepted by the author or publisher for any conditions or injuries resulting. While it is never inappropriate to contact a medical doctor, a visit to the piercer may be just as beneficial. If you have any doubt about how your piercing is healing, contact a reputable piercer or seek medical advice immediately.

Chapter Ten...

If things go wrong

WHERE A PIERCING is carried out by a properly trained and competent piercing operative, and a suitable aftercare routine is rigorously followed, then the experience, in most cases, is enjoyable and trouble free. Sometimes piercings don't go according to plan and, when this happens, it is helpful to know what to do.

Piercing stages and responsibilities

Stage	Who's responsible?	Time spent
Stage 1 – Pre-piercing decisions inc: finding a piercing operative and selecting the piercing type	Your responsibility to select the information and make the choice	Several days, weeks or months
Stage 2 – The piercing	Piercing operative's responsibility	15–30 minutes
Stage 3 – Aftercare Day-to-day care of the piercing, identifying possible complications, selecting new jewellery	Your responsibility to maintain the health of your piercing, observe any changes and seek any help	The life of your piercing

Poor placement or misalignment

If your piercing is 'wonky' and you didn't ask for it that way, you should immediately inform the piercing operative of your concerns. Likewise, if for any other reason you are unhappy with the piercing, you should return to the piercing operative who carried out the procedure and explain your concerns. If you are unhappy with the explanation, you may well want to seek a second opinion. Be aware, if this becomes the case, that there are different schools of thought on piercing styles and competence. Just because one piercing operative uses a different way of piercing, it doesn't make that method wrong.

Scarring

Once you have had a piercing, some kind of scarring is going to occur. The extent of any scarring, should you choose to remove your jewellery, will depend on a number of factors. Scarring generally increases, the longer the piercing is in place, and is worsened with complications, such as infections, migration, jewellery embedding and keloids.

Although generally scars are small, the effect they have will depend on their location on the body. Usually facial scars are more noticeable than the scar from a closed navel piercing.

Localised severe swelling and trauma around the piercing site

Localised swelling should be expected with all fresh piercings. Some parts of the body are more prone to swelling than others. The tongue and eyebrow particularly are prone to severe swelling. In some cases minor bruising occurs, producing a yellow to purple colour on the skin.

Jewellery embedding

This occurs where the skin between the piercing swells more than the distance allowed for. Typically, the skin in between the piercing becomes red, tight and painful. In more severe cases, the ring of a BCR begins to cut into the skin, or the balls at the end of the barbell start to pull into the wound, becoming 'embedded'. Most swellings occur during the first few days, or when the flesh around the piercing either becomes aggravated by pressure or develops an allergic reaction to a substance. Immediate action is required. The jewellery needs to be removed and replaced with a piece with a longer internal diameter.

If your piercing develops a physical abnormality, such as becoming painful, bleeding or discharging pus, do not delay in contacting your piercing operative. If they are not available, or the advice you receive doesn't appear satisfactory, then consult your regular doctor. Always bear in mind that doctors are rarely trained to deal with piercing wounds. If the symptoms are alarming and excessive, seek immediate emergency medical attention. Doctors are the right people to see in these circumstances.

Allergic reaction

The skin around a piercing can experience an allergic reaction to many things including jewellery metals – usually nickel alloy – and cleaning solutions. This can be avoided by wearing only low-nickel jewellery, such as titanium, and patch testing before applying any solutions onto your piercing. Allergic reactions can vary from a mild itching and faint reddening of the skin, to a burning and throbbing pain with swelling and a discharge of pus. Allergic reactions are often mistaken for infections.

Migration and rejection

When body jewellery moves from its original location through the skin, this is called migration. If the migration continues until the jewellery passes out through the skin, it is called rejection. The speed and severity of movement vary. Where jewellery moves quickly to a new comfortable position, it is described as parking. Some piercings, like the eyebrow, are more prone to migration.

Localised infection – sepsis or urethritis; blood poisoning (septicaemia)

Blood poisoning is rare in body piercing. Regularly carrying out a thorough post-piercing aftercare routine will help ensure that such risks are minimal. Touching the piercing with unwashed hands and bathing in infected water are two of the main causes of infection.

Chondritis

A rare inflammation of the cartilage due to bacterial infection. This is very difficult to treat successfully. For this reason, at the first sign of an infection in a nose or ear piercing, seek advice from your piercing operative or doctor.

Removing jewellery

When jewellery is removed from a piercing it first heals from the outside. With an infected piercing this is likely to lock the infection inside the piercing wound and can cause the formation of an abscess. Always check with a piercing operative before you permanently remove any jewellery.

Blood loss

New piercings don't necessarily bleed. When they do, the blood flow normally stops within a few minutes after piercing. With some piercings, such as tongues and genitals, occasional bleeding lasting only a minute or two can occur for a few days after the piercing. With all new piercings, activities which might induce further bleeding, including rigorous movement and exercise, should be avoided for at least 48 hours immediately afterwards. These include dancing, sports and other forms of physical exercise. Ingesting substances that are likely to thin the blood, such as alcohol and aspirin, should also be avoided for 72 hours before and after having a piercing.

If you experience any bleeding from your piercing after leaving the piercing premises, follow these guidelines:

Stay with a friend

Make sure that you have someone with you. If you do not, telephone a relative or a friend and explain the situation. They should telephone you every 30 minutes to ensure that you are still fine.

Apply pressure

Apply pressure using clean tissues or linen to the area around the entry and exit holes of your piercing for at least 20 minutes, or until the bleeding stops.

Seek emergency assistance

If after 20 minutes excessive bleeding continues, seek immediate medical attention at your local Accident and Emergency Department and, in the case of oral piercings, ask to be referred to the maxillofacial surgeon.

Seeking advice from a medical practitioner

An experienced and reputable body piercing operative will know when a piercing complication is beyond the scope of their expertise and will then refer you to a medical practitioner.

Not all doctors and medical personnel approve of body piercing, and sometimes their personal view of body piercing can influence how they treat you. They have a vast amount of knowledge about matters relating to the human body. Their training, however, doesn't yet include the healing of body piercings.

In general, medical training assumes that the safest course of action in treating a wound is to remove any obstruction. Seen in these terms, the jewellery in a piercing may be regarded as an obstruction in the wound. To the piercee, the jewellery is an adornment purposefully placed in the body. The object of piercing is to trick the body into accepting this foreign object (body jewellery) and healing around it. Most piercing complications can be treated without the permanent removal of the jewellery.

The removal of body jewellery from an infected piercing can lead to further complications.

When attending a medical professional with a piercing complication it is very helpful if they have either a good grasp of how piercings heal or have access to an experienced and reputable body piercer with whom they can consult.

Oral piercings

Oral piercings located in the constantly wet environment of the mouth may have their own problems and are listed separately from other piercings. They may include:

Infection

An infected oral piercing will display signs similar to those for other piercings and the immediate advice of a piercing operative and doctor should be sought. If neither is immediately available, visit your local Accident and Emergency Department.

Airway obstruction secondary to swelling

If the tongue swells, making it difficult to breathe, go directly to the nearest casualty department, and ask to be referred to the maxillofacial surgeon.

Aspiration of jewellery

To help lessen the risk of breathing in or swallowing jewellery it is very important to carry out regular tightness checks of jewellery balls on barbells and labret studs.

Embedded jewellery through excessive swelling

The jewellery fitted should be of sufficient length to allow for extreme swelling. If the tongue swells and the jewellery is becoming tight and the balls of the jewellery are starting to move into the tongue, contact your piercing operative to arrange for the jewellery to be removed. In severe cases, or if part of the jewellery becomes dislodged and you may have swallowed or inhaled it, go to your nearest casualty department and ask to be referred to the maxillofacial surgeon.

Prolonged bleeding

Prolonged bleeding in body piercing is very rare. The concern with bleeding from piercings inside the mouth is that the blood may mix with saliva and be swallowed unnoticed. In the case of the tongue, apply pressure to the piercing holes at both the top and bottom using clean linen, for example a handkerchief, for up to 20 minutes. If the bleeding does not stop, go immediately to casualty, and ask to be referred to the maxillofacial surgeon.

Chipped or fractured teeth

Poor sized and badly placed oral jewellery can lead to problems with teeth and gums. It is important that, in the case of a tongue piercing, the jewellery is not fitted too far forward where it can rub on teeth and gums. For this reason any replacement jewellery should not be too long. Habits where oral jewellery is rubbed against the teeth should be avoided.

Nerve damage and paraesthesia

Sometimes with a tongue piercing temporary loss of sensation in part of the tongue can be experienced. Where this occurs, sensation normally returns after the swelling leaves. If symptoms of paraesthesia occur at any time, seek advice from a piercing operative or dentist.

Changing your mind and removing a piercing

If you remove body jewellery, a scar will be left on the skin. Usually, the shorter the time that the jewellery has been in the skin, the less scarring will occur. If jewellery is removed within 24–48 hours after a piercing, it might bleed. To reduce the possibility of serious blood loss it is best therefore to leave the piercing jewellery in place for at least 48 hours before removing it. There are always exceptions to this rule and, for this reason, you should always consult a piercing operative or a medical professional before removing jewellery.

Chapter Eleven...

Common piercing complications

ENERALLY, BODY PIERCINGS heal without any problems, although some people can experience complications. These vary from a reddening of the skin or a mild itching sensation to, in rare circumstances, an infection. When complications occur in a piercing it is often difficult to obtain help and advice that will both protect your health and maintain your piercing. This section aims to take away some of the uncertainty in piercing complications and is based upon a combination of vast professional experience, common sense, research and extensive clinical practice. This information should not be considered a substitute for medical advice from a doctor or dentist, and any complication should be thoroughly investigated by both piercing and medical experts. Be aware, however, that many doctors and dentists have no specific training, or experience, regarding piercing and may not be educated on how best to assist you.

Listed below are some piercing complications which sometimes occur, along with a description of the probable cause, and some suggestions as to a possible remedy.

General complications
Complication: **A small split has occurred in one of the piercing holes**
Probable cause: Jewellery that is too long for the piercing may snag on clothing and can cause small tears in the skin.

Possible remedy: Apply warm saline solution 2–3 times each day as well as fitting a shorter barbell or smaller BCR.

Complication: **The piercing holes are red and dry**
Probable cause: Initially, a longer piece of jewellery is fitted into a piercing. When the swelling reduces, the jewellery can become too long and catch on clothing and cause irritation.
Possible remedy: Have your piercing measured and if necessary fit a smaller barbell. Until it heals, avoid wearing tightly fitting clothing, with belts and buckles that might push against your piercing.

Complication: **A pale yellow discharge is crusting on the skin around the piercing holes and on the jewellery**
Probable cause: This is the normal result of your body discharging plasma and exudation, and it will often cause the jewellery to fix tightly to the skin.
Possible remedy: Continue with a regular aftercare routine. If the discharge is smelly, darkens in colour or becomes painful to touch, then the piercing may be infected. In such a case, follow the instructions found in chapter 9 of this book for treating an infection and seek immediate medical advice.

Complication: **The skin under the piercing jewellery is raw**
Probable cause: The most likely cause is that the piercing has swollen beyond the size of the jewellery.
Possible remedy: If the jewellery looks like it is too tight/small for the piercing, longer jewellery may need to be fitted. Avoid tightly fitting clothing that can put pressure on the piercing. Apply warm saline soaks three times daily, and keep the piercing dry and ventilated.

Complication: **A mound of red/purple coloured skin is forming around the piercing hole**
Probable cause: These may be keloid scars. Some people are susceptible to them. Blood circulation in keloid skin is less efficient than in normal skin, and may slow down the healing process. Swelling can occur, making the jewellery tight and painful.

Possible remedy: Visit your piercing operative to have a longer, possibly PTFE, barbell fitted. Apply saline soaks three times daily. If you do not have a history of keloid scarring, check the piercing for other complications such as an infection.

Complication: **My jewellery is working itself out through my skin**
Probable cause: The body is rejecting the jewellery and this could be caused by a metal allergy, too shallow a piercing, or by the jewellery being too long or large.
Possible remedy: If metal allergy is suspected, fit a piece of alternative jewellery, such as, in the case of nickel allergy, titanium or a non-metal such as PTFE.

Complication: **A dark yellow/brown coloured pus with a distinct odour is discharging from the piercing and it is painful to touch**
Probable cause: This is usually the sign of an infection.
Possible remedy: Follow the instructions for treating infections in chapter 9 of this book. Seek immediate medical assistance.

Complication: **A small blister is forming close to the piercing**
Probable cause: Often the skin is purple in colour, soft and sometimes painful to touch, usually indicating the formation of an abscess.
Possible remedy: Compress a hot towel on the affected area for a few minutes, until it starts to cool. Then place an egg cup of warm saline solution over the area for 10–15 minutes four times daily. The compress opens up the pores, and drains the infection. Consult your doctor.

Complication: **The skin is tight, red and shiny with no discharge**
Probable cause: This is often the result of over-cleaning and may also be the result of regular vigorous exercise causing over-perspiration.
Possible remedy: If over-cleaning, reduce the frequency to 2–3 times daily and, in cases of over-perspiration, wear an absorbent dressing during exercise. Check for early signs of an infection.

Complication: **The skin is moving away from the jewellery and there is a red itchy rash**

Probable cause: Likely to be an allergic reaction. Check for metal allergy and for allergy to any cleaning solution being applied.

Possible remedy: Change to suitable alternative metal or plastic jewellery and change the cleaning solution.

Complication: **The jewellery has moved away from its initial position**

Probable cause: Effects of clothing, posture and daily habits impact upon a piercing. The jewellery can sometimes settle into a position that is more comfortable, and this is called jewellery 'parking'.

Possible remedy: Consider if any of your actions are affecting the piercing and attempt to reduce their impact. If the new 'parking' position is aesthetically unattractive, consider re-piercing.

Complication: **Feeling light headed, or faint immediately after being pierced**

Probable cause: Usually the result of your body experiencing shock, it can be aggravated by poor ventilation, standing too quickly, or not having eaten for some time.

Possible remedy: At the first signs of dizziness or a hot flush, sit or lie down and let someone know you are feeling unwell. Take slow deep breaths. In the case of diabetes, you should have already informed your piercing operative of your condition and have handed them some form of sugar glucose to use in such an eventuality.

Complication: **My piercing is bleeding**

Probable cause: For the first few days after having a piercing it can produce an occasional small bleed. This is sometimes caused by jewellery movement and snagging.

Possible remedy: Treat all new piercings with extra care. Any regular constant and heavy bleeding should be treated with suspicion and medical attention sought. See 'Blood loss' in chapter 10 of this book.

Piercing – specific complications – **Navel**

Complication: **The top piercing hole has become sore, painful and wet**

Probable cause: Often the result of pressure from clothing and every-day movement, or sleeping position. In severe cases the top holes become enlarged and the jewellery embeds in the skin.

Possible remedy: Have the piercing measured for a longer barbell. If wearing a BCR, change to a barbell. Apply warm saline solution 2–3 times daily. Avoid wearing clothing with tight waistbands, or large belt buckles.

Complication: **At the bottom of the piercing hole, a small piece of red and raw flesh is appearing**

Probable cause: The fleshy material is over-granulated skin tissue, and is the result of jewellery movement, causing the unformed fistula to be drawn out of the piercing. This occurs more commonly where a barbell is lifted as part of a play habit or to allow room to clean inside the navel.

Possible remedy: Stop lifting the jewellery to clean or play. Apply saline solution four times daily using the egg cup method. Visit your doctor to check for a secondary infection and the possibility of having the granuloma cauterised.

Piercing – specific complications – **Oral**

Complication: **My tongue is taking on a white/light brown colour**

Probable cause: Possibly over-use or over-concentration of a mouth-wash solution which may have caused a fungal infection.

Possible remedy: Change to saline solution for mouth rinsing.

Complication: **A tear is appearing alongside the jewellery of the lip piercing**

Probable cause: Too small a diameter or too fine a gauge BCR is fitted.

Possible remedy: Change to a larger internal diameter BCR, or to a labret stud with, in both cases, a minimum of 1.6mm gauge.

Complication: **The flat plate of the labret has sunk into the lip**
Probable cause: Too short a piece of jewellery is fitted.
Possible remedy: Visit a piercing operative to have a longer labret stud fitted.

Complication: **The outside of the top lip is becoming soft and swollen**
Probable cause: Usually the result of wiping perspiration or mucus discharge from the nose. Tends to be worse when suffering from a cold, etc.
Possible remedy: Wash the affected area 2–3 times daily with saline solution. Apply a suitable moisturising cream with added vitamin E. Check for metal allergy and possible infection.

Piercing – specific complications – **Tongue**

Complication: **Small ulcers are developing on the roof of the mouth and under the tongue**
Probable cause: Too long a barbell is rubbing the lining of the mouth and gums, or the piercing is poorly located.
Possible remedy: Apply an over-the-counter topical gel. Visit a piercing operative to have the piercing checked for location or to have a shorter barbell fitted.

Complication: **The tongue has a small split on its top edge alongside the piercing**
Probable cause: This is usually the result of wearing too long a barbell.
Possible remedy: Have a shorter barbell fitted.

Complication: **The jewellery balls have sunk into the tongue**
Probable cause: This is usually accompanied by a painful throbbing in the tongue. This is because the tongue has swollen more than was anticipated.
Possible remedy: The barbell needs immediate removal. Visit a piercing operative so that the piercing can be assessed. If there are no

signs of an infection or an allergic reaction, and the swelling is not likely to cause asphyxiation, then a longer barbell can be fitted.

Complication: **A small fleshy lump has appeared on the tongue around the piercing hole**
Probable cause: Usually white in colour and not accompanied by any pain or discomfort, this is usually due to friction movement of the bar forming a temporary granuloma (fleshy lump).
Possible remedy: It usually falls away naturally after a few days. If not, have it checked. Rinse with saline solution four times daily.

Complication: **Pus is discharging from one or both of the piercing holes and it is painful to touch**
Probable cause: The piercing may have become infected. Check the section in chapter 4 on metal allergies to eliminate this.
Possible remedy: Treat as an infection and seek immediate medical assistance.

Piercing – specific complications – **Eyebrow**

Complication: **The upper eyelid looks like a 'black eye'**
Probable cause: This can happen with some eyebrow piercings. The bruising travels downward with gravity to the thin skin of the eyelid.
Possible remedy: If not accompanied by any other symptoms, it normally fades after a few days.

Piercing – specific complications – **Ears**

Complication: **The skin is growing around my jewellery**
Probable cause: A granuloma or keloid is probably forming and can be caused by wearing too small a BCR.
Possible remedy: Change to a larger ring, a labret stud or barbell and apply warm saline compresses four times daily.

Complication: **The ear is painful, swollen and purple in appearance**

Probable cause: These are signs of fluid retention and a possible infection.

Possible remedy: Treat as an infection and seek immediate medical attention. Prolonged untreated infections of ear cartilage can lead to a condition called chondritis, which is very difficult to treat. Applying a warm saline compress can bring some relief.

Piercing – specific complications – **Nipple**

Complication: **A hard, painful lump has formed under the skin at the back of the piercing**

Probable cause: This could be the result of an infection that has become trapped under the skin and is causing the formation of an abscess. Any swelling under the skin left untreated can lead to further complications.

Possible remedy: Visit your doctor and ask for a thorough investigation to be carried out. If, after treatment, the lump remains without an explanation as to the cause, then insist that further investigations be carried out.

Please note

The advice given in this section is based on the author's research, practical experience and consultations with piercing operatives and medical professionals. However, the information is given for guideline purposes only and no legal responsibility can be accepted by the author or publisher for any conditions or injuries resulting. While it is never inappropriate to contact a medical doctor, a visit to the piercer may be just as beneficial. If you have any doubt about how your piercing is healing, contact a reputable piercer or seek medical advice immediately.

Chapter Twelve...
The future

URING THE 1980s, the combination of the first piercing studios with the regular supply of specialist quality piercing jewellery provided the catalyst for the Western piercing renaissance. This re-birth has brought about a new trade and, with it, the advent of the modern day body piercing practitioner. At the core of this piercing renaissance are individuals who maintain high standards of piercing techniques, and rigorously implement scrupulous hygiene and infection control procedures.

In sharp contrast to these high standards and this professionalism are the negative media reports that focus on the number of piercing infections. These reports are often unbalanced, not taking into consideration the massive increase in the number of piercings. An estimated 1.5 million piercings were carried out in 1995, increasing to over 10 million by the year 2000. Given this increase, it is understandable that the number of reported piercing complications should also increase. But, when these complications are reported in the media without stating the massive increase in the number of piercings, it gives the impression that body piercing is suffering from worsening standards, which is not necessarily the case.

There are always improvements that can be made in any trade. Likewise there will always be people, who will cut corners in order to make a fast buck. Major reforms are in progress to implement a minimum national standard for the trade, as well as a qualification backed by the British government.

The consumer can play an important role in maintaining and improving piercing standards. Public health officials might have faith in legislation, but they lack resources to ensure that it is enforced. Well-informed, pro-active members of the public, making safe choices about who pierces them, and how and with what they are pierced, will always be the most powerful force in the marketplace.

A piercing heals differently from an ordinary skin wound. This difference is gradually being learned by general practitioners and hospital staff who are now softening their attitudes towards those who present themselves with piercing complications. The days when your GP declared in disdainful tones, 'This is a self-inflicted wound and the jewellery should be removed at once!', are quickly and thankfully becoming a thing of the past.

Skin piercing is an acceptable part of fashion. As more people become pierced, attitudes throughout Western society are changing. A strong indication of this acceptance is in the proposed regulation by the Establishment. With regulations come integration and acceptance.

In this modern age of the global media, whatever is Western very quickly becomes a worldwide fashion. In developing countries wannabe Westerners desire everything from pop music and denim jeans to text messages. Many of the aspiring Westerners live in countries where, for generations, their own indigenous peoples have maintained piercing traditions. These practices have often been disowned by the minority cosmopolitan nouveaux riches as being undesirable and representative of a failed system of living. Instead they look to the Western pop stars and fashion icons as their new social idols. Ironically, the wearing of piercing jewellery is now seen as being an essential requirement to becoming Westernised. It's only going to be a matter of time before the Dayak tribesmen of Borneo order their next ampallang barbell from a Western body jewellery catalogue!

Chapter Thirteen...

Commonly used piercing terms

THIS GLOSSARY CONTAINS names and terms commonly used in body piercing, as well as offering explanations of terms and phrases used in this book.

Add-on
Something extra used to add to a piece of jewellery in order to customise it. Often add-ons are referred to as decorative shields which are added to jewelled navel bars.

AIDS
Acquired Immune Deficiency Syndrome. A potentially fatal disease spread through cross-contamination of body fluids, such as blood, clear body fluids from a wound, semen and vaginal fluids.
See also HIV.

Alcohol wipe
A pre-packed, isopropyl, alcohol-soaked piece of fibre, used to wipe the skin prior to a piercing.

Alignment
For most piercings it is very important that the jewellery should fit vertically, horizontally, centrally, etc. This is called alignment.

Anaesthetic
A substance that is used to reduce the sensation of pain.

Anaphylaxis

When the body produces an extreme reaction to contact with a substance either on the skin, or taken into the body. Often causes the person to exhibit symptoms of restricted breathing, swelling, low blood pressure, rapid pulse, collapse, and can be fatal if left untreated. The reported incidents of anaphylactic shock are on the increase. In piercing, the dangers of anaphylactic shock are greatest where anaesthetics are used. Immediate treatment is vital – usually with an injection of adrenalin.

Anatomy

Understanding the structure of the body.

Antibiotic

A medicine that either kills bacteria or prevents its growth.

Antiseptic

Used in piercing to help destroy potential disease-causing micro-organisms and to help reduce the risk of infection.

Areola

The darker coloured skin area surrounding the nipple.

Aspiration

The breathing in of an object into the lungs. Any oral piercing carries this potential risk.

Autoclave

A device used to sterilise piercing equipment and jewellery used in body piercing. It needs to be regularly maintained to ensure that it is working properly. It is the only way to ensure that piercing equipment and jewellery are properly sterilised.

Bacterial infection

Bacteria are microscopic organisms that may cause disease in an unhealed piercing wound.

Body Shock
An international jewellery manufacturer producing high quality body jewellery.

Cartilage
Flexible body fibres that support the construction of the ears and nose. Blood supply in cartilage is poor and can lead to slow healing when pierced.

Circumcision
In men, this involves the removal of the foreskin of the penis. In women, it may involve the removal of the clitoris. This is often done for reasons of religion and tradition as well as for medical reasons.

Clamp
A device used in piercing, designed to hold the skin around the piercing site during the procedure. Also known as forceps.

Closing-up
If you take jewellery out of an unhealed piercing and leave it out for only a few hours, it can close up. Even if the piercing is a few months old you may have difficulty getting your jewellery back in place if it has not healed properly.

Complication
Usually referred to in piercing when a problem occurs in the healing process of the piercing wound.

Cross-contamination
Where body fluids containing viruses are transferred from one person to another.

Crust
The hard plasma residue that builds up around the outside of a piercing wound.

Cubic Zircons

Abbreviated to 'CZ'. A naturally forming mineral gemstone. Through a commercial process it is available in many colours and shades. Commonly used to decorate fancy body jewellery, such as the popular Jewelled Navel Bar, or JNB for short.

Customised

Adding extra pieces to a standard piece of body jewellery. For example, fitting jewelled balls onto the end of a plain barbell.

Disclaimer

A verbal or written statement made by the piercee that usually limits the piercing operative's responsibility for the piercing procedure, and waives their responsibility for the post-piercing circumstances. It is usually subject to the piercer carrying out certain minimum standards of safe practice during the procedure. The validity and interpretation of such an agreement is subject to individual circumstances and local law.

Disinfectant

A chemical used in piercing to kill and control the spread of a micro-organism that might otherwise cause disease in a piercing wound.

Dorsal corona

Located on both sides on the top rear smooth surface of the penis glans.

Ear tapers

A tapered cylinder made from metal, wood or acrylic which is used to gradually stretch and enlarge an ear lobe piercing.

Enlarging crescent

Metal tapered bar bent into a crescent shape, starting from a narrow gauge at the point and becoming thicker as the crescent progresses. Used for stretching piercings. Also known as a stretching crescent.

Epithelisation
See healing period.

Exhibitionism
Many people who have piercings enjoy having people look at them, enjoying the shock that is sometimes caused.

Fainting
This is a temporary loss of consciousness due to insufficient oxygen reaching the brain. Fainting in piercing is sometimes caused by pain, but more generally by stress brought on through fear of pain. If fainting is going to occur, the symptoms appear within the first 10 minutes after the piercing. The symptoms of fainting are blurred or dimmed vision, dizziness, nausea, ringing in the ears, sweating and a feeling of weakness; they are worsened by a stuffy, poorly ventilated atmosphere. At the first sign of any of these symptoms, the onset of fainting can be prevented by laying down on one's back with the legs raised.

Fear
It is normal to experience a level of fear before having a piercing. The level of fear will exhibit through varying degrees of anxiety, from mild butterflies in the stomach to physical shaking. This fear can lead in extreme cases to post-piercing fainting.

Fistula
The medical term to describe the artificial tube or tunnel of flesh that is formed in the body when a piercing has healed.

Flaccid
When erectile tissue is soft and wrinkled and not firm, such as in the nipple and the penis.

Flesh tunnels or tubes
A type of jewellery used to fit into enlarged ear lobe piercings. Made from hollow tubes with raised rims to keep them in place. Also known as eyelets and earlets.

Forceps
See clamps.

Foreskin
Popular name for the prepuce, the loose fold of skin that covers the glans of the penis when it is flaccid and which retracts during erection.

Fraenulum
A fleshy flange of skin located on the underside of the penis which connects the foreskin and the penis glans. The fraenulum doesn't always remain after circumcision.

Fraenum
A layer of supporting muscle tissue that holds an organ in place. An example of this is under the tongue: the fraenum is seen as a long thin line running from front to back on the underside. Also, the name sometimes given to a piercing of the fraenulum.

Fresh piercing
See initial piercing.

Gauge
One of the three critical dimensions involved in measuring piercing jewellery, the others being the internal diameter and internal length. The gauge is the thickness of the straight rod in a barbell, or round rod in a BCR. It is crucial that the correct gauge jewellery be fitted into a piercing.

Gay
See homosexual.

Gel
Clear water lubricating gel that can be used to help ease the passage of jewellery into a piercing. Essential when using an instrument to stretch a piercing or when 'up-sizing' with larger gauge jewellery. Can be purchased from most pharmacies.

Genitalia or genitals
The name given to the male and female sexual organs.

Granulation
A small extension of flesh at one or other of the piercing holes, most commonly occurring in new piercings. This skin tissue has a high concentration of blood vessels giving it a red 'raw' appearance. Also, referred to as a polyp. With such a complication, a visit to your piercing operative or doctor is necessary.

Healed piercing
When a piercing is healed inside and out and a fistula has prop- erly developed between the two holes. For most piercings, this process takes at least 16 weeks and, in some cases, far longer.

Healing period
The medical name for this period is epithelisation. This period varies from person to person based upon individual circumstances and from one piercing type to another. See also epithelisation.

Hepatitis
A viral infection that causes an inflammation of the liver and can be debilitating or even fatal.

HIV
Human Immunodeficiency Virus. The carriers of this virus can develop AIDS. See also AIDS.

Homosexual
Someone who is sexually attracted to members of the same sex.

Hoop
Another name for a BCR.

Horizontal

Refers to the alignment of the piercing holes. Horizontal piercings are located crossways from side to side (in a straight line, east to west).

Horns

See tusks.

Hygiene

The procedures that are applied in body piercing studios to control the spread of infectious diseases.

Hypersensitivity

Where a person has an extreme sensitive reaction to a substance. This could be a compound used in a metal alloy, such as nickel in metal body jewellery. In severe cases, a reaction to an oral anaesthetic could lead to a fatal anaphylactic shock.

Hypo-allergenic jewellery

To reduce the chances of the body rejecting the piercing jewellery it is important to select hypo-allergenic jewellery. Good examples of this include titanium, niobium and PTFE.

Indigenous population

The native population of a country. In piercing, indigenous populations are often referred to as the native peoples of countries whose culture appears to be less technologically advanced than in Western countries.

Inert

An inert piece of jewellery, such as titanium, when placed in the body, will not cause a chemical reaction.

Infection control

The hygiene procedures used in piercing to restrict the spread of micro-organisms.

Initial jewellery

It is very important that the correct material composition and size of jewellery be used in a fresh piercing. Initial jewellery should be low in nickel content: in the European Union countries, that means 0.05 per cent maximum permissible level of nickel. The internal dimension of the jewellery should allow for swelling of the flesh around the piercing site.

Initial piercing

A term used to describe a new piercing. Also described as a fresh or new piercing.

Internal diameter

For BCR jewellery, the internal distance measured across the centre of the circle.

Internal length

Refers to the internal length of a barbell style piece of jewellery. It is the distance measured in between the inside edges of the two external balls.

Insertion pin

See tapered insertion pin.

Inverted nipple

Medically considered to be an abnormality. In some cases, a nipple piercing is reputed to be a possible cure for this condition.

Keloid

A build up of excessive scar tissue. It is often darker in colour than the surrounding skin and can appear reddish purple in colour. It has a poor blood supply which often prolongs the healing period.

Latex gloves

An important barrier in the process of infection control, they are worn by the piercing operative during piercing procedures. A new pair should be worn for every client and be replaced several times during a procedure, particularly when they make contact with a potential contaminate, such as the floor, a door handle, or after scratching an itch.

Mainstream

This is a very broad term used to describe what is acceptable to the vast majority of the population within a society. Body piercing is seen by this kind of measurement as being on the fringes of society.

Medical wipe

Sometimes called medi-wipe. See alcohol wipe.

Micro-organism

A very minute organism that can't be seen with the naked eye. Identified by microscope, micro-organisms include bacteria, fungi, prions, protozoa, viruses and yeasts.

Minor

Someone who has not reached the age of majority or adulthood. In the United Kingdom this is 18 years of age. In some European countries they can be younger and, in some states of America, it can be as late as 21 years.

Oral

This refers to piercings in the mouth such as the tongue, and includes piercings that travel from the inside of the mouth to the outside: for example, lips and cheeks.

Pain

A localised sensation which can range from mild discomfort to an unbearable and excruciating experience.

Parental consent

A person under the age of majority (see minor) needs the permission of their parents.

Parking

This describes when jewellery moves itself to a new position. This may not be the most desirable location but is usually where it is most comfortable.

Penis

The male sex organ through which urine and semen pass.

Penis glans

The smooth area of the penis head. Revealed in un-circumcised men when the foreskin is retracted.

Perineum

Located behind the genital organs and in front of the anus.

Piercee

The person receiving the piercing.

Piercing dimension or distance

The measured distance between two piercing holes.

Piercing operative

The name given to someone who performs piercing procedures.

Piercing procedure

The process of carrying out a piercing.

Piercing size

This is the measurement between the two piercing holes. This measurement represents the size of the internal measurement of any jewellery that is to be fitted into the piercing hole(s).

Placement

This is where the jewellery is placed through the skin.

Plug

A solid cylindrical piece of jewellery with a raised outer rim to keep it in place. Intended for wear in enlarged ear lobe piercings and made from acrylic, metal, wood, minerals and other materials.

Polyp

A common term used to describe a granulation complication on a piercing wound.

Post-piercing

The period of time after the piercing has been completed.

Post-piercing aftercare

The routine and procedure used in caring for the piercing wound.

Posture

In piercing this relates to any regular bodily movement that may cause irritation or damage to a piercee.

Pre-piercing

The period of time before having a piercing.

Primitive people

See indigenous population.

Rejection

The body's natural processes' attempt to reject any foreign bodies that enter the skin. When this happens to a piercing it is called rejection.

Reputable piercing operative

Someone who has established a good name for piercing to a high standard.

Retainer

A piece of jewellery, often made of clear plastic, which is worn in a piercing to make it less noticeable.

Ring

Another name for a BCR

Rite of passage

An event or statement marking a transition from one stage of life to another. It may be shared with others in the form of a ceremony or be a private personal statement.

Rod

The commercial name given to a length of metal that is round in section.

Sado-masochistic sub culture

Collective name for a broad group of individuals who share a common, often voyeuristic, desire to live out their private and shared fantasy dramas in acts of extreme exhibitionism, some-times sexually violent in content. Body piercing often plays a role in these experiences.

Satisfaction note

The paperwork signed by the piercee after having had a piercing, confirming their satisfaction with the piercing and procedure.

Scab

The crust that forms over a skin wound. Scabs that crust on the skin, but do not attach to the jewellery, should be encouraged in order to develop a healthy piercing.

Scrotum

The pouch of skin hanging behind the penis and containing the testes.

Septicaemia

Commonly known as blood poisoning. This condition occurs where the bacterial infection spreads into the blood. It is more likely in individuals whose immunity has been lowered through illness. It is a very rare body piercing complication.

Scroll
The folded metal plate drilled to fit at the back of the ear on an ear stud post to hold the jewellery in the piercing.

Septum retainer
A less noticeable piece of jewellery worn to keep the piercing hole open in the septum piercing of the nose.

Sexual assault
In piercing, a charge of indecent or sexual assault could technically be brought against a piercing operative who pierces the sexual organs of a minor.

Sexual intercourse
An act of sex where the penis is inserted into the vagina.

Shield
A decorative attachment commonly added to standard jewelled navel bars and nipple barbells to make them more attractive.

Spikes
Tapered lengths of metal and plastic used to replace balls on barbells.

Springs
Projecting cone-shaped metal springs designed to be attached to nipple jewellery. Sometimes called whirls.

Sterile
A germ-free state. In piercing it is extremely important that all equipment and jewellery used be sterile.

Sterilisation
Describes the process of the complete destruction or removal of living micro-organisms.

Steriliser

A device used to sterilise piercing equipment and jewellery used in body piercing.

Swelling

The flesh around most piercings experiences some swelling shortly after being pierced. The amount of swelling varies between people and piercing locations. This will usually return to normal within a few days or weeks.

Tapered insertion pin

A tapered metal instrument used to re-open or stretch the diameter of a piercing. It is a rod which narrows to one end. It is hollow at the larger end to enable a larger piece of jewellery to be safely inserted into the piercing.

Trade

A group of workers who have developed a recognised skill in carrying out a particular form of work. The collective name for those carrying out the practice of skin piercing can be considered to be the trade of body piercing.

Tusks

Worn in pairs to replace balls at the ends of barbells. They may vary in gauge and length. With septum and bridge nose piercings they can be used to dramatic effect.

Ultrasonic cleaner

An important device that helps maintain adequate levels of infection control in body piercing practices. It is used prior to sterilisation to release debris from piercing instruments and jewellery by emitting high frequency sound waves. The debris is then dissolved in an enzyme fluid.

Umbilical cord

The rope-like connection that supplies oxygen and nutrients to the unborn baby. The cord ceases to function at birth and is cut. It then shrivels and forms the navel scar (belly button).

Unhealed piercing

A piercing that has not fully healed. It may appear to be fully healed externally, but, inside, the fistula is not fully formed.

Urethra

The tube by which urine is excreted from the bladder.

Urine

Provided that you are healthy and free from any kidney infections, your piercing is not at risk from your own urine. Your own urine can help clean away bacteria from your own genital piercing wound.

Vernier gauge

A device which is used in body piercing to measure distance and locate the points for marking the position of the piercing holes, as well as measuring length and gauge of jewellery. Also called a micrometer or wheel gauge.

Vertical

When referring to alignment, this indicates that the piercing holes sit in a straight upright line, one above the other (North to South).

Virus

The smallest known type of infectious agent. It needs to enter another organism in order to reproduce. This can happen if a virus enters a piercing wound. Piercing operatives need to maintain stringent procedures of control to prevent the spread of viruses.

Vitamin C

Also known under the chemical name ascorbic acid. Naturally occurring in citrus fruits and green vegetables, Vitamin C can help aid the body's natural healing process. If taking medication, check that there are no interactions between your medication and Vitamin C. For example, the absorption of the contraceptive pill can be delayed by Vitamin C.

Waiver

See disclaimer.

Wooden stretchers

A tapered sphere that is made of wood and is used to enlarge a piercing. Usually used for stretching an ear lobe piercing.

Wound

When the skin is pierced and jewellery inserted, a wound is formed.

Zinc

A trace element that helps with the healing of wounds. Found naturally in wholemeal breads, wholegrain cereals and dried beans. Can be taken as a supplement to assist natural bodily healing processes.

Chapter Fourteen...

Frequently asked questions

When can I change my jewellery? – You should only remove the initial piercing jewellery after the piercing has healed. This is normally at least four months after the initial piercing, although this does vary.

How soon after piercing can I go swimming? – A piercing is an open wound and you should treat it as such. Going into a body of water with an open wound always carries a risk of infection. While your piercing is unhealed, this risk applies. Therefore it is best to cover your piercing with a secure waterproof dressing before going swimming.

How long will it take for my piercing to heal? – Most piercings take at least four months to heal, although some oral piercings may heal sooner, and if a piercing suffers a complication it can take even longer.

If I leave my jewellery out for a few days, will it close up? – The simple answer is yes. How long this takes depends upon where on the body it is located, and the length of time the piercing has been in place. Oral piercings tend to close most quickly and fresh piercings close more quickly than older ones.

The bar on my navel jewellery keeps sticking out at the top and catching on my clothes. Why is this? – The barbell is too long. All initial piercings are fitted with longer pieces of jewellery to allow for swelling. When the swelling goes down, the jewellery needs replacing. Over   ıe a piercing can gradually shrink and may need a shorter bar fitted.

I keep biting my tongue bar when I eat. What should I do? – Because the swelling in a tongue piercing is unpredictable and can be severe, a much longer barbell is fitted in a new piercing. After 7   days, this needs to be replaced with a shorter one. Barbells may need to be gradually shortened over the following months. Leaving too long a barbell in a piercing can lead to complications, such as chipped teeth or sore gums.

When can I fit non-sterile jewellery? – It is safest never to fit non-sterile jewellery and it should never be worn in an unhealed piercing.

When is it safe to use steel jewellery? – Steel jewellery with greater than 0.05 per cent nickel content should only be worn after a piercing has healed and not before, and should never be worn in a new piercing.

Does it matter what size jewellery I wear in my piercings? – The size of your jewellery is very important to the health of your piercing. Only correctly-sized and -fitted jewellery should be worn.

Is it safe to share jewellery with my friends? – It is definitely not safe unless the jewellery has been thoroughly cleaned and sterilised in an autoclave. If the piercing is not healed, blood-borne infections, such as hepatitis, can be transmitted from one person to another.

I have been told that boys should have their right eyebrow pierced and girls the left. Is this correct? – Both males and females commonly have either or both eyebrows pierced.

Do only gay men have their navels pierced? – No. Both gay and straight men have their navels pierced. This is becoming a very popular heterosexual male piercing.

Is it OK to French kiss with a tongue piercing or other oral piercing? If the piercings are unhealed, the risk of transmitting infectious blood-borne disease is increased.

INDEX

DIY Publishing

You brought your baby into this world, how do you want it to grow -up?

If you have a book to publish and want to have a stronger input into it's production whilst maintaining control of 'your baby's' design, production, distribution and decide how it will be marketed to the public, then a talk with one of our self publishing consultants might be the next step.

Advice and services available on;
Financial budgeting, design, typesetting, page formatting, proof reading, printing, distribution, marketing, press releases and media campaigns.

For a Free consultation
Email: Publishing@nliten.co.uk

Tel: + 44 (0) 23 9237 7099

or visit the NliteN International Publications web site:
www.nliten.co.uk

About Mark Eames
the author of **BODY PIERCING – "Does it hurt?"**

In 1996 his 13 year old daughter asked to have her belly button pierced. Neither of them realised what a catalyst for change it would prove to be, leading to Mark exchanging a career in Architecture, for an adventure into the realms of body piercing. The journey thus far has involved him meeting, talking with and piercing thousands of people, and has resulted in him writing this book.

His eye for precise detail, coupled with an ability to create solutions to complex situations, has enabled him to bring together a vast wealth of information, creating this easily understandable and well presented comprehensive guide.

The growth of body piercing as an emerging popular practise continues to cause concern amongst some sectors of Western society. By helping to make people aware of the key health and safety issues associated with body piercing he is creating an environment where body piercing can be both safe and fun. He sits along side expert piercers, medical doctors and scientists who together are addressing these important concerns.

As a result of these efforts he is helping to co-ordinate the introduction of a land mark qualification in body piercing. The course will require that students achieve 100% competence in procedures in order to achieve a pass certificate. It is scheduled to be made available to students through colleges of further education and other institutions during 2002.